For Jill, Mum and Dad, without whose
love and support this project would never
have been possible

IMAGES FROM
A WARMING
PLANET

ASHLEY COOPER
IMAGES FROM A WARMING PLANET

ONE MAN'S MISSION TO DOCUMENT CLIMATE CHANGE AROUND THE WORLD

Previous pages:

Death Valley, California, USA.

Blue hue. An Iceberg off Curverville Island on the Antarctic Peninsular.

Storm clouds gathering over Cumbria.

Contents

Foreword

This is a book about change. About the way the climate is already changing, and the way in which it will change even more dramatically in the future. About changes in people's lives as they seek to make sense of weather systems that seem to have slipped those reassuring bounds of normality and predictability. About changes in our understanding of what's going on around us, in our world views, in our orientation both to our current reality and to the future. And by and large, people really don't like change.

As Ashley Cooper says in his Introduction:
'An Inuit whose lifestyle is uniquely tied to the rhythms of nature and the seasons doesn't need a scientist to tell them that their Arctic environment is changing rapidly. In the span of a human lifetime, Inuits have witnessed the change in the Arctic sea ice, in the same way that a Polynesian Islander has seen the level of the sea gradually rise to a point where their coral atoll is inundated on a regular basis. Climbers who have for generations scaled alpine peaks have watched the glaciers recede back up the mountainside at an alarming pace.'

Most people coming into contact with this wonderful book will be several generations removed from the physical immediacy of lived experiences of that kind. Indeed, most people in rich world countries today are increasingly distanced from any 'rhythms of nature', with fewer and fewer people working on the land in any way, and more and more locked into urban or suburban lifestyles where 'nature' is predominantly something to be 'consumed' via breathtakingly vivid films and TV programmes.

I've long been persuaded that this pervasive 'alienation effect' is one of the most important reasons why we find it so hard to make sense of the daily 'laying waste' of the natural world around us. We are no longer at home in our own earthly home; there is concrete and steel that comes between us, a seductive but spurious super-abundance of technology, and the discord of distorted reason.

But in order to be at home in the world, we must be fully in it, experience it directly as mud between our toes, as the rough bark on a tree, as the song of the world awakening every morning. I still believe the Earth speaks to something in every person, even when we are imprisoned by all that concrete and steel. And in that dialogue lies a form of celebration as primitively powerful as anything to

Above:
The weather is a-changing. A thunder storm passing
over the Langdale Pikes in the Lake District, UK.
As the climate warms, the atmosphere can hold greater
quantities of water vapour, leading to an increase in
both frequency and intensity of heavy rainfall events.

be found in our anaemic, rootless culture – reflected, often in the loss of that dialogue, in many of Ashley's images.

It's that alienation effect, moreover, which explains why citizens of the rich, urbanised world haven't (as yet!) risen up in a paroxysm of rage to demand political responses that are truly commensurate with what the science of climate change now tells us. How, otherwise, would we still be headed 'gently into that dark night' of potentially irreversible climate change?

Writing this in January 2016, we can (and must!) take some hope from the historic Agreement signed in Paris in December 2015. After two weeks of predictably fraught negotiations, 196 world leaders declared unambiguously that the overarching purpose of the Agreement is to limit the average increase in global temperature to 'well below 2°C', 'to pursue efforts to limit that increase to 1.5°C' – the first time such an ambitious (and scientifically justified) target has been included in any climate change agreement – and to eliminate net greenhouse gases entirely sometime between 2050 and 2100. All of which means, in effect, bringing down the curtain on the age of fossil fuels.

But for most people that's still just so much hot air from politicians who have failed and failed again to translate fine words into firm action. Rather more important, I suspect, is the infinitely more visceral experience of people impacted, in their own back yards, by their very own climate-induced disaster. And what began in the North of England at exactly the same time as the Paris Conference, is certainly one of the most telling examples of this. For the best part of a month, the Lake District (which just happens to be Ashley Cooper's own stamping-ground) and much of the rest of the North of England was battered by one storm after another sweeping in from the Atlantic – Storm Desmond, Storm Eve, Storm Frank. (see pages 101-107). Politicians blathered on about 'one in a hundred years events' and unprecedented extremes – all of which was of mighty little comfort to people who'd heard it all before just a few years ago.

It's the frequency of such events that scientists are most concerned about. And their ubiquity. In just the last six months, floods have been experienced in Russia, Dominica, Oman, Sweden, Utah, Oregon and Washington in the USA, Sierra Leone, New Zealand, Turkey, Greece, Italy, Croatia, Bosnia, Tamil

Nadu, Norway, as well as the North of England and Scotland. And that's just the record on flooding. The same kind of picture emerges when one looks at other extreme weather events including droughts, wildfires, hurricanes, storm surges and so on.

Astonishingly, I now hear more and more people describing all this as 'the new normal' – when what they should be saying, on each and every occasion, out loud and very loudly, is that this is the new, devastatingly awful abnormal, getting more and more abnormal by the year, progressively stripping away any reasonable prospect we might once have had of a safe and stable climate.

So, please, do not 'flick through' this extraordinary photographic record as just another 'snapshot in time'. Do not be tempted into any kind of passive voyeurism; do not allow the power of the images to come between you and the people whose changing lives they portray. See it more as a declaration of solidarity, and as the powerful call to action that it surely is.

Jonathon Porritt

Introduction

I set out thirteen years ago with one simple aim, to document the impacts of climate change on every continent. In that time I have been privileged to see many amazing sights and meet many incredible people. I have seen hope and despair, and more views of earthly destruction than I care to remember.

This book is not about the science of climate change, there are thousands of such important works already out there, rather it is about the art of climate change. By holding up a camera to document the change that I see around me, I hope I have produced a record that will firstly convince people that climate change is real, and secondly that we are running out of time to do anything about it. If the images in this book motivate people to action, then it will all have been worth it. We need the science to inform us of the changes going on all around us, but my journey has been more about the changes that we can all see happening, if we choose to look. An Inuit whose lifestyle is uniquely tied to the rhythms of nature and the seasons doesn't need a scientist to tell them that their Arctic environment is changing rapidly. In the span of a human lifetime, Inuits have witnessed the change in the Arctic sea ice, in the same way that a Polynesian islander has seen the level of the sea gradually rise to a point where their coral atoll is inundated on a regular basis. Farmers can tell you that the rainfall patterns have altered over their land, sometime for the better, but usually for the worse. The Chinese peasant farmer who used to grow enough food to support their family in Inner Mongolia, has had to abandon their land as the desert has swept over it, rendering it uninhabitable. Climbers who have for generations scaled Alpine peaks have watched the glaciers recede back up the mountainside at an alarming pace. Who hasn't noticed the fact that the weather is changing, that once stable weather patterns are breaking down and being replaced by ever more powerful events. Floods are increasing in both frequency and intensity as are forest fires, droughts, desertification, coral bleaching events, permafrost melt. The list is almost endless, but it is in these less than subtle changes, obvious for all to see that my project has been grounded.

As well as the doom and gloom of a climate changing world, I have chosen to focus my lens on the many mitigation measures which can be easily adopted. Renewable energy technologies have mushroomed in recent years, showing us that we can power our lives without destroying the stable climate in which humanity first developed and flourished. Iceland is a great example, where 100% of their electricity is generated by renewables, 30% from geothermal and 70% from hydro. Humanity has loaded the atmosphere with CO_2 to levels that the planet has not seen for around 15 million years. Much of this book is dedicated to the consequences that this is having. If I have learnt one thing in my travels it is that those least responsible for climate change, are most impacted by it. Rich western communities have a certain degree of resilience afforded by wealth, a luxury that the poorer communities of the world do not have. Climate change is the greatest threat that humanity has ever faced, I hope this book will go some small way to motivate change.

Above:
Ultimately all the earth's energy comes from the sun.
We have a responsibility to use it wisely and sustainably.

Right:
Human culture evolved and flourished in a world with a relatively stable climate, where the average levels of CO_2 in the atmosphere were 350 ppm. The burning of fossil fuels have pushed the levels of CO_2 up to over 400 ppm. The Broch of Gurness in Orkney, on mainland island was thought to have been constructed between 100 and 200 BC. The central defensive tower or Broch is surrounded by small stone dwellings. Later Pictish houses are also to be found on the same site. The site is also believed to have been used by the Vikings.

Following page:
At the going down of the sun.
Planet Earth is amazingly beautiful and we all have a duty to protect it. The setting sun illuminates a magical landscape over Great Gable, from Red Screes in the English Lake District, UK.

Fossil fuels

The exploitation of easily reached fossil fuel reserves, coal, oil and gas has released vast quantities of CO_2 into the atmosphere. At the start of the industrial revolution, climate science was either none existent or poorly understood. The exploitation of coal, the first fossil fuel to be used extensively, lead to known air pollution, culminating in the awful smogs that brought London to a standstill, and killed thousands in the 1950's. The Clean Air acts that followed did much to clean up the airbourne pollutants that caused the damaging smogs, but did little to stem rising CO_2 emissions. It was only in the 1980's that climate change started to be noticed, and only since the turn of the century, 15 years ago, that climate change started to move up the political agenda. Climate science is now clearly understood, but we continue to burn our way through fossil fuel reserves, as if this had no impact. In the last couple of years a divestment campaign has emerged that has tried to persuade institutions to withdraw their money from fossil fuel companies. A change has started, but it is still too slow, and possibly too late. The latest research shows that if we are to stand any chance of keeping under a 2°C rise in temperature then over 90% of US and Australian coal and almost all of the Canadian tar sands, must stay unexploited, in the ground. Only by moving rapidly to a low carbon economy can we expect to stabilise the earth's climate at levels at which human civilisation emerged and flourished, and which all biodiversity of the planet relies.

Right:
The carbon footprint of travel. Traffic congestion on the M1
motorway at Loughborough due to sheer volume of traffic,
with a plane coming into land at East Midlands Airport.

Left:
The boiler at Queen's Mill in Burnley, UK. The mill is powered by a steam engine, built over 100 years ago and is still powering the mill today. The weaving shed at Queen's Mill was used as a location for filming the Kings Speech. At one time the Lancashire cotton industry clothed the world. The steam powered industry, fuelled by coal, was the start of large scale carbon emissions, which set us on the road to anthropomorphic climate change. In its hey day, the boiler was consuming six tons of coal a day.

Following page:
Emissions from a Petrochemical works at Seal Sands on Teeside, UK.

Above:
The RAF Red Arrows flying over the Lake District during the Windermere Air Show, UK.

Left:
A fleet of oil tankers leaving the Persian Gulf near Dubai.

Following page:
Flaring off waste gas back lights steam from the Ineos oil refinery at Grangemouth in the Firth of Forth, Scotland, UK. It is Scotland's only oil refinery. It takes oil from a pipeline from the Forties North Sea production area, and processes 10 million tonnes of crude oil a year. As such it is a large contributor to climate change.

Left:
Emissions from the Tata steel works in Ijmuiden, Netherlands.
Steel production is extremely carbon intensive, using vast quantities
of coal.

Above:
Emissions being released into the atmosphere from a
Petrochemical works at Seal Sands on Teeside, UK.

Previous page:
Emissions from the Ineos oil refinery at
Grangemouth in the Firth of Forth,
Scotland, UK, at dusk.

Right:
Coal moving machinery at Port Waratah,
the world's largest coal port, Newcastle,
Australia. Coal from open cast mines in
the Hunter Valley is exported around the
world, especially to China. Australia relies
on coal for generating the majority of its
electricity. Australians individually also
have the world's largest carbon footprints.

Following page:
The Beltana number 1 mine, an open
cast or drift coal mine managed by Xstrata
Coal in the Hunter Valley, New South
Wales. If we are serious about tackling
climate change, coal, the dirtiest of fossil
fuels, needs to be kept in the ground.

Left:
Lorries haul coal past a coal fired power plant in
Dongsheng, Inner Mongolia, China.

Above:
A Chinese peasant scavenges for coal in order to keep
warm. The coal that has fallen from lorries taking it
from an open cast coal mine to power plants near Heihe
on the Chinese-Russian border.

Above:
A new coal fired power station being constructed
in Inner Mongolia, China. Worryingly, China is building
a new coal fired power station every week and has
huge reserves of coal, much of which is very low
grade and highly polluting.

Above:
Slum dwellings in Suihua, Heilongjiang Province
pump out coal smoke into an already highly polluted
atmosphere. Rates of heart and lung disease, and
breathing difficulties are commonplace in Chinese
cities, that are amongst the most heavily polluted
in the world.

Above:
The chaos of coal. Ratcliffe on Soar coal fired power station near Nottingham, UK, responsible for massive greenhouse gas emissions.

Above:
Is this any way to treat our life support systems?
A farmer sprays cabbages with pesticide in front of a
test drilling site that is fracking shale for gas near
Southport, Lancashire, UK.

Above:
A Gaschem ship full of LPG sails into Teesmouth harbour past the Redcar Steel works, Teeside, UK.

Right:
Centrica's gas plant in Barrow in Furness. This plant processes gas from the Morecambe Bay gas field, Cumbria, UK.

Above:
Waste oil leaks from abandoned barrels on the tundra
at Nome in Alaska.

Left:
A biker in the Kern River oilfield in Oildale, California,
USA. Following an unprecedented four year long drought,
Bakersfield is now the driest city in the USA. Still many
Americans fail to make the connection between their
addiction to fossil fuels and climate change.

Above:
An oilfield in Taft, California, USA. Many of the oil wells in this area have been fracked, and a sign clearly shows that this industry isn't just bad for the climate.

Left:
The oil men are obviously too busy making money to make the connection between their activities and the desperate drought conditions that surround them. The Kern River oilfield in Bakersfield, California, USA.

Above:
An utter waste. Flaring off gas at the Flotta oil terminal on the Island of Flotta in the Orkney's, Scotland, UK.

Left:
Oil workers drilling a new oil well in the Daqing oil field in Northern China.

Following page:
Oil pumps in the Daqing oil field in Northern China.

Previous page:
Oil is used to make a myriad of plastic products, many of which ultimately end up in the sea. Here they litter the tide line in Assynt, Scotland, UK.

Above:
Traffic on Euston Road in front of the iconic St Pancras Railway Station, London, UK.

Right:
Rush hour traffic at sunset on the M60 motorway near Manchester, UK. Consumption of one gallon of petrol emits around 10.2 Kg of CO_2.

Following page:
Cars in Dubai in the Middle East. This rapidly expanding city has been designed around car transport, with petrol prices cheap, in this oil rich state.

Above:
A jet engine with a contrail from another jet in the background. In the European Union emissions from aviation increased by 87% between 1990 and 2006. On average air travel is around ten times as carbon intensive as car travel.

Left:
A plane taxiing towards arrivals at Manchester Airport, UK.

Top:
Expensive petrol prices in Billingham on Teeside, UK, with an electricity pylon. This stark image taken at dusk seems to sum up our addiction to energy.

Above:
A couple viewing Melbourne city at night from the viewing platform in the Eureka Tower, Australia. Looking down upon the illuminated city highlights the amount of energy used to power a modern lifestyle.

Left:
Our cities use vast amounts of energy, much of which is wasted, River Thames and Houses of Parliament, London, UK.

Above:
Light pollution. Ambleside from Wansfell Pike in the Lake District UK, with street lighting leaving an orange glow on the mist.

Right:
The Bellagio Fountain on Las Vegas Boulevard. Las Vegas is probably the most unsustainable city in the world, it uses huge amounts of water in the middle of a desert and vast amounts of energy to power its famous illuminated displays.

Above:
An electric tram at the world famous Blackpool
Illuminations, Lancashire, UK. A great spectacle but
one which uses a lot of energy.

Above:
In a world with finite resources, surely it makes sense
to save fossil fuels for serious uses that really need
them. An injured climber with a dislocated shoulder is
winched off Jacks Rake on Pavey Ark in the Lake
District by the Langdale/Ambleside Mountain Rescue
Team and an RAF Sea King Helicopter.

Tar sands

Of all mans efforts to exploit fossil fuels, the Canadian tar sands are by far the most environmentally destructive, and as such are worth singling out for particular attention. The tar sands are a mix of bitumen, sands, clays and gravels. They are only economically viable to exploit when oil prices are at the higher end of their range. They can be turned into synthetic oil, but only by separating out the bitumen from the sands and gravels. They are exploited in two ways, depending on how close to the surface the deposits lie. Deposits close to the surface are strip mined. This involves clear felling the Boreal forest leading to the second fastest rate of deforestation on the planet, second only to the rates in the Amazon rain forest. Each 2.5 square Km of Boreal forest supports 500 breeding pairs of migrant birds, as well as being home to Wolf, Lynx, Cougar, Black Bear, Grizzly Bear, Wolverine, Bison, Moose, Caribou and Beaver. It is also an important carbon sink. The first problem is that it destroys vast swathes of valuable wildlife habitat and eradicates a vital carbon sink. Secondly the soil overburden has to be removed. Syncrude (one of four oil companies operating in the area) has removed more earth than that moved by the Great pyramid at Cheops, The Great Wall of China, the Suez Canal and the world's ten largest dam projects combined. Once the overburden is removed, massive mining machinery works 24 hours a day to dig the tar sand out. The third problem arises when you process the tar sand. In order to be able to separate the bitumen from the sands and gravels, the tar sand needs to be melted. This is achieved by forcing steam through the mix. The amount of gas used to make the steam, means that the resulting oil has a carbon footprint up to five times that of conventional oil, making it a climate change disaster. Fourthly, when the steam condenses back to water, it contains many toxic pollutants from the bitumen. The waste water is discharged into unlined tailings ponds that leach toxins out into the Athabasca River. These flow downstream and seriously impact the health of First Nation Canadians living downstream. Rates of skin disease and rare cancers in these communities have risen steeply, since the tar sands mining started.

The second way in which the tar sands are exploited, is when they lie too far from the surface to be strip mined. They are then exploited via SAGD mines, standing for steam assisted gravity drainage. Two pipelines are drilled vertically, one to the top of the tar sands layer and one to the bottom. The pipes then spread out horizontally. Vast quantities of steam are pumped down the upper pipe

Above:
A dragonfly stuck in tar sand.

Following page:
A brand new tar sands plant being constructed
near Fort McMurray.

and out into the tar sands layer. The steam melts the bitumen which then flows down due to gravity and is sucked up by the lower pipe. The steam is generated by burning natural gas. It takes 1,200 cubic feet of gas to produce one barrel of synthetic oil. It produces 45Kg of CO_2 per barrel of oil produced making it the most carbon intensive oil on the planet.

Whilst documenting the tar sands, I was hassled and intimidated every step of the way, by both oil company security guards and the Royal Canadian Mounted Police (RCMP). Presumably, because they don't want the world to see the devastating destruction they are wreaking in the north of Canada. On my first day of photography, I was stopped by an RCMP officer, who informed me that if I took one step off the highway, he would arrest me for trespass. I asked him what would happen next, and was told that I would be locked away in a cell, until such a time that a judge saw fit to look at my case, probably around three to four months. I laughed at the guy and said. 'You can't be serious. You can't imagine a less serious crime than trespass, and you would lock me away on remand for several months, for stepping one foot off the highway'. He looked me straight in the eye and said 'yep'.

My problems were as nothing compared to Dr John O'Connor who spent years working in First Nation communities downstream of the tar sands industry. He started to find unusual rates of rare cancers amongst the locals. One cancer in particular, Cholangio carcinoma (bile duct cancer) normally affects 1 in 100,000 people. John found six cases in Fort Chipewyan a community of 1,200 people. When Dr O'Connor raised his concerns and a possible link to the tar sands industry, he expected the government to launch a community wide health survey. The government's reaction was to charge him with four cases of professional misconduct. 1. Engendering mistrust. 2. Blocking access to patient files. 3. Billing irregularities. 4. Raising undue alarm in the community. John spent four years fighting to clear his name and was eventually completely exonerated of all charges by the Board of Physicians of Alberta. A clear sign that Canada will not allow anything to get in the way of their exploitation of the tar sands.

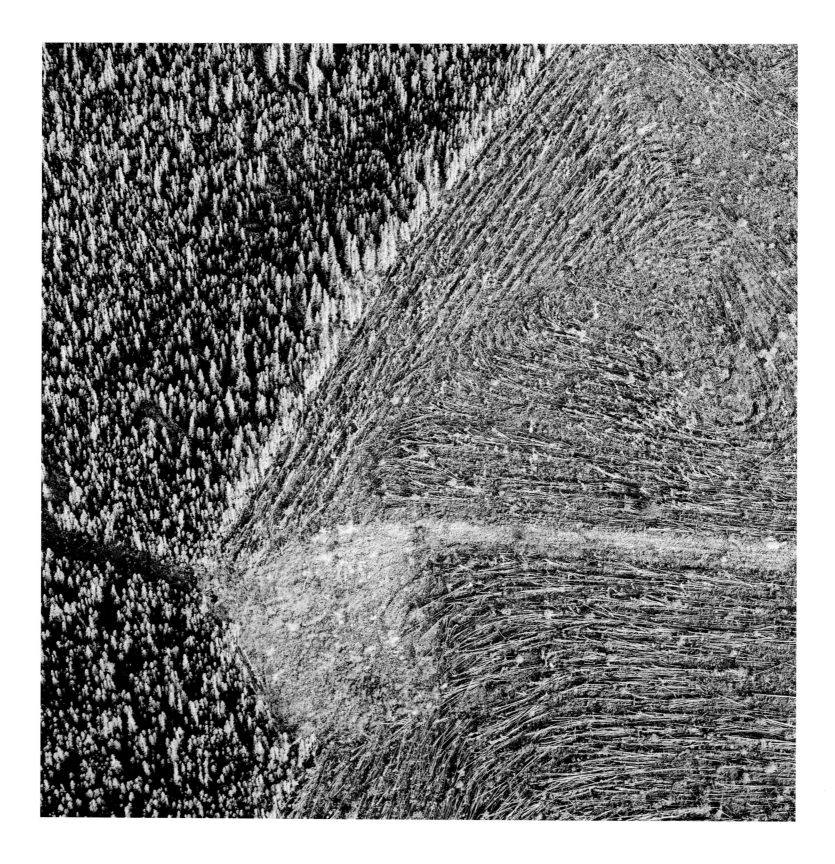

Adjacent page:
Boreal forest trees clear felled to make way for a new tar sands mine north of Fort McMurray, Canada. Each 2.5 square Km of Boreal forest supports 500 breeding pairs of migrant birds, as well as being home to Wolf, Lynx, Cougar, Black Bear, Grizzly Bear, Wolverine, Bison, Moose, Caribou, and Beaver. As well as a valuable wildlife habitat, it is also an important carbon sink.

Top left:
Massive tailbacks on Highway 63 north of Fort McMurray, the capital of the tar sands, caused by tar sands workers returning from work.

Below left:
Environmental madness. Suncor, one of the main tar sands oil companies operating in Athabasca, Alberta, Canada. The tar sands are the largest industrial project on the planet, and the world's most environmentally destructive. The synthetic oil produced from them is 3 times more carbon intensive than conventional oil supplies, a disaster for the climate. They are responsible for the second fastest rate of deforestation on the planet. They produce millions of litres of highly toxic water every day which leaches out into the Athabasca river and has serious health impacts on First Nation peoples living downstream.

Above:
Heaven and Hell. Tar sands deposits being mined North of Fort McMurray, Alberta, Canada.

Above:
Matchsticks. Boreal forest trees clear felled to make
way for a new tar sands mine north of Fort McMurray,
Alberta, Canada.

Above:
Yellow mountain. Sulpher extracted from
the raw bitumen from tar sands is piled
up in huge mountains by the Syncrude
upgrader plant near Fort McMurray.
The digger gives you a sense of the scale.

Right:
Strangely hypnotic. A tailings pond at
the Syncrude mine. These highly polluted,
unlined ponds leach toxic chemicals into
the surrounding environment. As the mines
lie on important bird migration routes
from Arctic breeding grounds to Southern
wintering quarters, thousands of wildfowl
a year are killed when they land on the oil
covered waste water lakes.

Left:
Oil is boomed off a tailings pond at the Syncrude mine. I used a helicopter to capture aerials, in order to appreciate the scale of the devastation caused by the tar sands mines. Taking to the air was the only time I escaped the attentions of security guards and Royal Canadian Mounted Police, who threatened me with arrest if I so much as took one step off the highway.

Below left:
The artists palette. Bizzare patterns in floating oil on a tailings pond at the Syncrude mine.

Below:
A hand full of raw tar sand. This gloopy mix of bitumen, sand and gravel is what the oil men are after. In order to separate the bitumen out, vast quantities of steam are forced through the mix to melt the bitumen. The steam is generated by burning vast quantities of natural gas. This is what gives tar sands synthetic oil its massive carbon footprint. When the steam condenses back to water, it contains many toxic, carcinogenic compounds. It is this filthy water that is put into the unlined tailings ponds. From there it leaches out into the Athabasca River, and contaminates everything downstream.

Above:
Ali Walker drives a large road rolling
machine at the Syncrude, Mildred Lake
tar sands plant. Like many workers,
Ali was attracted by the huge salaries
on offer in the tar sands. She used to be
a baker and now jokes she rolls roads
rather than dough. A dump truck driver in
the tar sands can earn $200,000 a year.

Left:
The rape of the land. Tar sands deposits
being exploited North of Fort McMurray,
Alberta, Canada. The activity carries
on 24 hours a day 365 days a year.

Following page:
Greed and destruction. Massive dump
trucks queue up to load with tar sand in
front of a toxic wasteland.

Top:
Andrew Knuff a tar sands worker relaxes during down time at one of many work camps that house tar sands workers. This particular camp houses 10,000 people.

Above:
A tar sands camp, north of Fort McMurray, which houses 10,000 workers.

Left:
Trash at the end of the rainbow. Trucks haul an oversize load of pipeline and tar sands equipment, on the road north to Fort McMurray, the centre of the tar sands industry.

Top right:
Dr John O'Connor has spent years working in First Nation communities downstream of the tar sands industry. He started to find unusual rates of rare cancers amongst the First Nation Canadians. One cancer in particular, Cholangio carcinoma (bile duct cancer) normally affects 1 in 100,000 people. John found six cases in Fort Chipewyan a community of 1200 people. When Dr O'Connor raised his concerns and a possible link to the tar sands industry, he expected the government to launch a community wide health survey. The government's reaction was to charge him with four cases of professional misconduct.

1 Engendering mistrust.
2 Blocking access to patient files.
3 Billing irregularities.
4 Raising undue alarm in the community.

A cynical attempt by the Canadian Government to silence him. John spent four years fighting to clear his name and was eventually completely exonerated of all charges by the Board of Physicians of Alberta. John with one of his patients, Clara Mercer. Clara is currently battling a rare kidney cancer and has had half of both her kidneys removed. She has lived in Fort McKay, downstream of the tar sands mines, all her life.

Bottom right:
Jean L'Hommercourt and her grandson Dez L'Hommercourt who both live in Fort McKay, downstream of the tar sands. Many residents suffer health problems,

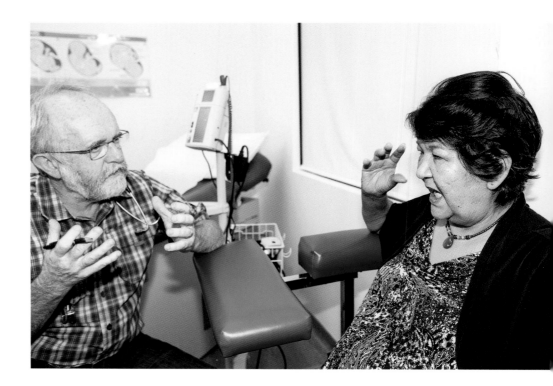

with the government refusing to launch an investigation that might implicate the tar sands industry. Dez was born with an under developed heart, similar to that found in many Russian children born after Chernobyl blew up. Dez is four years old and has already had four major operations on his heart.

Top left:
Vitaline Jenner a First Nation Canadian who lives in Fort Chipewyan uses state of the art gym equipment sponsored by oil money. The town is on the Athabasca river and lake downstream of the tar sands mines. Suspicious numbers of people in Fort Chipewyan have died of cancer and many of the buildings in Fort Chipewyan have been sponsored by tar sands oil companies in an attempt to buy the communities silence.

Bottom left:
A fish caught in Lake Athabasca by Robert Grandjamber. Robert lives in Fort Chipewyan, a First Nation community downstream of the tar sands industry. Many of the residents of Fort Chipewyan have died of cancer. Fish caught in the lake recently have been found with tumours and lesions and many people are now scared to eat this traditional food source. The fish processing plant in Fort Chipewyan has been closed down due to the concerns.

The weather is a-changing

All the latest climate modelling programs show that our extreme weather events will become both more frequent and aggressive. This makes perfect sense. Heat is the energy that drives all of our weather, the more heat you add to the system, the more power you will get out.

As our rainfall is ultimately derived from water evaporating from the oceans, the warmer the oceans the greater the degree of evaporation, and the more extreme our heavy rainfall events become. Unless we take rapid and drastic action to curb CO_2 emissions we can all look forward to many more extreme weather events, and ever spiralling costs in terms of infrastructure damage. Some areas will get a lot wetter leading to increased catastrophic flooding, others will get drier leading to vast swathes of land becoming unsuitable for agriculture. As well as impacting agriculture, drier conditions are leading to far more frequent wild fires. These changes have already been observed by many places around the planet. You don't need to be a climate expert to notice that the weather patterns are changing.

Right:
Displaced flood children in Baani refugee camp
near Phalombe, Malawi.

Above:
On Friday 20th July 2007 up to 5 inches
of rain fell across central and southern
England on already saturated ground. It
caused this landslide due to the weight
of water in the super saturated ground,
blocking the A44 west of Worcester, UK.

Right:
Whitehaven Harbour being battered by
extreme storm waves, Cumbria, UK.

Above:
After 2 days of storm force winds the Irish Sea on the West coast of Cumbria at Whitehaven was whipped up into a fury, creating vast quantities of spume.

Above left:
Blackpool being battered by storms on the 18th January 2007 that killed 13 people across the UK in the hurricane force winds. I had to hold onto a lamp post to get this shot, otherwise I would have been blown down the promenade. The UK has seen a marked increase in frequency and intensity of storms, causing huge damage and costing the insurance industry billions.

Below left:
After a week of high tides, storm surges and storm force winds, the promenade of Aberystwyth in Wales has been devastated, with £Millions worth of damage. The crashing waves punched a large hole in the sea wall and collapsed Aberystwyth's iconic, Victorian promenade shelter, which has stood for over 100 years. This picture was taken on Wednesday 8th January, 2014, the day the council started to try and clear the thousands of tonnes of beach rubble off the sea front road.

Above:
An RAF Sea King Helicopter prepares to drop salvage experts onto the River Dance washed ashore off Blackpool. The River Dance was one of three ships lost that day off the UK. The ship was hit by a huge wave that shifted the vehicle cargo on the decks causing the ship to list violently. The crew were airlifted off by RAF helicopter before the ship ran aground. As climate change takes hold more and more damage is occurring as the weather becomes more violent.

Left:
Crashing fury. Two days of storm force southerly winds whipped up the sea battering the Orkney mainland coast, with waves crashing over the 80 foot cliffs of Mull Head on Deerness.

Above right:
The 2014 winter storms damaged much of the UK coastline, revealing an unexpected bonus on Walney Island. A clay bed revealed by the coastal erosion was found to contain these two large antlers, held by Mathew Lipton. Belonging to a long extinct species of deer, they are thousands of years old.

Below right:
The January 2005 storm that lashed Western Scotland claimed the lives of five people. Huge waves totally destroyed these harbour side buildings in Mallaig, Scotland. The waves were higher than any ever recorded in Mallaig.

Far right:
On November 11th 2010 a deep low pressure crossed the Atlantic and slammed into the North West coastline. Winds of 100 mph battered the coast and caused around £1 million worth of damage to the iconic Blackpool illuminations.

Top right:
In January 2005 a severe storm hit Cumbria with over 100 mph winds that caused havoc on the roads and toppled over 1 million trees. These Sycamore trees were snapped like matchsticks in the hurricane force winds.

Bottom right:
Climate justice. The same storm toppled this tree onto a Chelsea tractor at Rydal, Cumbria, UK.

Top left:
Lorries toppled like dominoes on the M6 motorway at Shap, Cumbria, by the January 2005 storm.

Bottom left:
These old Oak trees in the Langdale Valley, in the English Lake District, had stood for over 100 years, but were no match for the January 2005 severe storm that toppled over one million trees.

Top right:
Mike Withers being blasted by spindrift during high winds moving snow above Grasmere in the Lake District, UK.

Bottom right:
A JCB tries to clear a way through massive snow drifts blocking the Kirkstone Pass road above Ambleside in the Lake District, UK during the extreme weather event of late March 2013. Counter intuitively, this severe cold weather is a direct consequence of climate change. As the Arctic sea ice melts, it alters the high pressure systems that normally dominate the Arctic in winter, pushing much colder air further south. Recent research has revealed that colder winters across much of Eurasia are now far more likely as a consequence of climate change.

Top left:
The Kentmere hills in the Lake District UK with Highland Cattle on the side of Kirkstone Pass. The livestock industry is the single largest emmitter of greenhouse gases on the planet. The biggest step anyone can take to reduce their climate change footprint would be to seriously cut down their meat intake, or become vegetarian, even better vegan.

Bottom left:
Upskiing on Great Dodd at 2,800 feet in the Helvellyn range, Lake District, UK. Such winter conditions were a rarity in the run of mild winters in the twenty years prior to 2009. It is distinctly possible that if the North Atlantic Conveyor breaks down (It is currently slowing due to the vast quantities of fresh glacial melt water entering the Arctic Ocean) that the UK could see much colder winters.

Following page:
The tarn on the summit of Red Screes in the Lake District, frozen solid by severe winter weather.

Above:
A snow plough on Dunmail Raise in the Lake District, UK, and a stranded motorist caught out by the extremely severe winter weather in the 2010 winter.

Left:
Derwent Water at Keswick in the Lake District completely frozen over during the December 2010 big chill, with tracks from a cyclist who biked across the lake.

Right:
In Ludlow, Gordon and Doreen Pearce who had lived in this house for 40 years had to flee for their lives as the River Corve undermined their house which then partially collapsed into the river.

Adjacent page, top left:
Liquid assets. A cash machine in Toll Bar, South Yorkshire, UK hit by unprecedented floods during June 2007.

Adjacent page, top right:
A marooned resident searches for food inside a flooded house in Toll Bar, South Yorkshire, UK hit by unprecedented floods during June 2007. The village was cut off for over a week.

Adjacent page bottom left:
Camper vans flooded in Tewkesbury.
On Friday 20th July 2007 up to 5 inches of rain fell across central and southern England on already saturated ground. Rivers rose rapidly and by Saturday flooding started to occur along the River Severn corridor. Tewkesbury in Gloucestershire was particularly badly hit where the rivers Severn and Avon meet. Rivers rose to unprecedented levels causing the worst ever floods. Thousands of homes were inundated, with people having to be evacuated many by boat or by Sea King helicopter The Myth water treatment plant in the town was flooded cutting off water supplies to around 350,000 people. Many also had their electricity supplies cut off as sub stations were affected. Estimates for the cost of the devastating and unprecedented summer floods are around £5 billion.

Adjacent page bottom right:
A young man cycles through flood waters in Toll Bar, South Yorkshire, UK

Above right:
On Thursday 19th November 2009 over 31cm of rain fell in 24 hours on the Cumbrian mountains. Until Storm Desmond in 2015, it was the single largest rainfall total in the British Isles since records began. It caused unprecedented flooding, with Cockermouth being particularly badly hit. The Langdale/ Ambleside Mountain Rescue Team responding to calls for help from flooded motorists, Ambleside, UK.

Below right:
A footbridge over the River Derwent in Workington, UK is one of many that was destroyed or damaged in the flood.

Far right:
The November 2009 floods in Cumbria caused £millions worth of damage, This house in Keswick next to the River Greta, collapsed after it was undermined by the flood waters.

Left:
Rescue workers carrying flood victims from
their houses on the Main Street of Cockermouth,
Cumbria, UK.

Top right:
Walking home. The same extreme rainfall event washed
away this van on flooded roads near Ambleside,
Cumbria, UK.

Bottom right:
The main street of Cockermouth five feet underwater,
with flooded cars, Cumbria, UK.

Above:
RNLI and Mountain Rescue volunteers
rescuing flood victims from their house on
the Main Street of Cockermouth, UK.

Right:
A flooded classroom in Trinity School,
Carlisle, UK.

Above:
Insurance claim. Cars that were totally submerged and written off by the January 2005 floods in Carlisle, after the River Eden burst its banks, Cumbria, UK

Above left:
Stranded. Pooley Bridge that spanned the River Eamont, below Ullswater had withstood the elements since it was built in 1764, but it was no match for Storm Desmond and was completely destroyed. Photo taken on Tuesday 8th December 2015, showing British Telecom engineers trying to restore communications to the other side, after they were cut by the bridge collapse, along with British Army soldiers. The storm set a new British record for rainfall totals in a day with 341.4mm falling in 24 hours.

Below left:
When the Lions roar. Environment Agency staff involved in pumping out floodwater from Hardwicke Circus in Carlisle, Cumbria on Tuesday 8th December 2015, after torrential rain from storm Desmond.

Previous page:
Reclaiming the lowlands. On Saturday 5th December 2015, Storm Desmond crashed into the UK, producing the UK's highest ever 24 hour rainfall total at 341.4mm. It flooded the Lyth Valley, drowning many farms and houses. Several periods of subsequent heavy rain have kept the Lyth Valley inundated, with no sign of respite. Photo taken on Thursday 10th December 2015.

Above:
Food Relief. Dave Freeborn of Patterdale Mountain Rescue Team use their rescue boat to take food supplies to Howtown on the other side of the Lake that had been cut off for five days by the floods.

Right:
The road that went for a walk. Tarmac in Glenridding washed sideways by the force of the floods, with a Patterdale Mountain Rescue Team Land Rover crossing.

Top right:
A caravan park that contained around thirty static caravans in Bolton, near Appleby, Cumbria, UK, all of the vans were damaged and many destroyed when the River Eden flooded as a result of Storm Desmond. The resulting damage will run into £hundreds of thousands on this one farm site.

Bottom right:
Boys toys. Storm Desmond created the worst floods the Lake District has ever seen, wreaking havoc on the roads. The A591, the main road through the Lake District was closed after parts of it were washed away and other parts were left under mountains of rubble washed onto the road from the slopes of Helvellyn. The Army was mobilised to help clear the road, which was closed for six months while the part that was washed away was repaired. Photo taken Sunday 13th December 2015.

Top left:
Cut off. Low Bridge End Farm in St Johns in the Vale, near Keswick, Lake District, UK, with their access bridge destroyed by the floods from Storm Desmond.

Bottom left:
Crop destruction. On Saturday 18th July 2009, 70 mm of rain fell over the North East UK onto already saturated ground. The river Wear burst its banks, inundating the floodplain around the city of Durham and flooding many properties.
As the water in the river started to drop, a section of the banking collapsed into the river. The flood water that was held back on the floodplain now suddenly had a shortcut back into the river. As the floodwaters tore back into the river channel they eroded a huge gully nicknamed by the locals as the Durham Canyon. The erosion feature is up to five metres deep, 30 metres across and 200 metres long. 12,000 cubic metres of soil were washed into the river from a field of Barley at Shincliffe near Durham.

Far left:
On Saturday 6th March 2010, Melbourne was hit by the worst tropical storm they had experienced in over 100 years. It started with a hail storm, with hail 12cm across (the size of lemons) followed by torrential rain. A$millions of damage was caused and many of the cities streets were flooded causing chaos to transport.

Above:
A cyclist on Melbourne's flooded streets.

Left:
Wading around Melbourne.

Pages 112-113:
In mid January 2015, a three day period of excessive rain brought unprecedented floods to the small poor African country of Malawi. It displaced nearly quarter of a million people, devastated 64,000 hectares of land and killed several hundred people. The scale of the destruction, with ruined farmland, is starkly visible from the air.

Pages 114-115:
Crops and precious soil washed away by the Malawi floods.

Pages 116-117:
Local farmers crossing their fields, which have been devastated by the floods, Malawi.

Far left, top:
Riverbank erosion. A house destroyed on a tributary of the Shire River near Chikwawa.

Far left, bottom:
Infrastructure damage. A destroyed bridge with the road washed away between Zomba and Phalombe, Malawi.

Above left:
Boys play on railway lines left suspended after the floods washed away the embankment, Lower Shire Valley, Malawi.

Above right:
Tree roots left exposed as the river bank was washed away near Chikwawa.

Left:
A massive tree undermined when the farmland soil was washed away around it, near Bangula, Malawi.

Right:
A boy stands in front of his house, one
of many destroyed by the floods, Bangula,
Malawi.

Adjacent page top left:
Sorrow. A grand mother and child in the
Chiteskesa refugee camp near Mulanje,
Malawi.

Adjacent page top right:
Flood victims in Baani refugee camp near
Phalombe, Malawi.

Adjacent page, bottom left:
Innocent. A girl in a refugee camp on the
Shire River near Chikwawa.

Adjacent page bottom right:
A boy injured in the floods in a refugee camp
in Bangula.

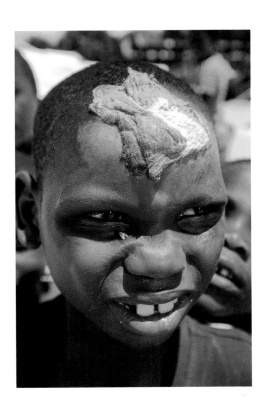

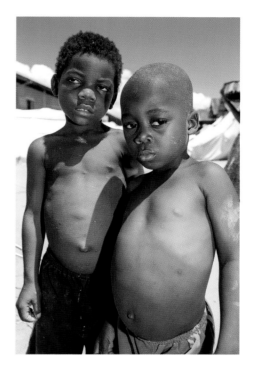

Left:
Children in Baani refugee camp near
Phalombe, in a maize field, Malawi's
subsistence food.

Above:
Malnourished children in a refugee
camp in Bangula. Malawi is one of the
poorest countries in the world with high
levels of child hunger, exacerbated by
climate change.

Left:
Children crowd around a Russian Mi8 helicopter being used by the United Nations World Food Program to deliver food aid to areas still cut off by the flooding, around Bangula and Mkhanga.

Top right:
Re-fuelling the aid helicopter prior to another mission.

Bottom right:
Medicins Sans Frontieres doctors awaiting an emergency flight to areas still cut off by flood waters.

Right:
A Malawian man with a butchered Hippo near Chikwawa, Malawi. As flooding washed away thousands of livestock, local people have been forced to turn to bush meat for food.

Adjacent page,top left:
A woman waits to see if her Malaria test will prove positive.

Adjacent page,top right:
A Medicin Sans Frontieres clinic in Makhanga testing local people for Malaria, many of whom proved positive for the disease. Rates of Malaria have rocketed as a result of the drying up flood waters providing ideal breeding grounds for mosquitoes.

Adjacent page bottom left:
A TV weather forecast, forecasting a heat wave in the UK. Science predicts that climate change will lead to far more frequent and severe heat waves. The 2003 heat wave that affected much of Southern Europe hit France especially hard, with estimates of deaths caused at 70,000.

Adjacent page bottom right:
The future. An extreme heat danger sign in Death Valley, California.

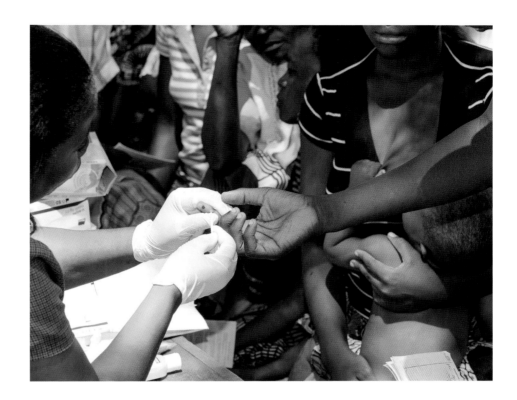

Left:
A dried up river bed in the Anti Atlas mountains of
Morocco, North Africa.

Above:
A well in the Anti Atlas mountains of Morocco, North
Africa. In recent years, rainfall totals have reduced
by around 75% as a result of climate change, leaving this
Barley, which should be ready to harvest, barely poking
out of the ground.

Previous page:
A 12th century grain store or Agadir at the Berber village of Tizgui in the Anti Atlas mountains of Morocco, North Africa. The grain stores were used to protect food supplies from warring tribes. Due to a 75% reduction in rainfall totals in this region, many of the villages have been abandoned, as it is no longer viable to grow crops.

Top right:
China is in the middle of its worst drought in 50 years. Many areas of Northern China are desperately short of water. This has lead the government to start a cloud seeding program to try and make it rain. Silver halide shells are fired into cloud with the microscopic particles acting as nuclei around which rain drops can form. This cloud seeding cannon is on the outskirts of Harbin City in Heilongjiang Province, Northern China.

Bottom right:
Sand dunes expanding and swallowing up forest in Shanxi Province in China. The province has been particularly badly hit by an ongoing drought with ever drier conditions and creeping desertification.

Adjacent page top:
Desertification in Shanxi Province which has been particularly badly hit by the ongoing drought, with the irony of a coal fired power station in the background.

Adjacent page bottom:
China is in the middle of the worst drought in 50 years. Precipitation totals have fallen significantly across most of China's northern provinces. 60% of

China's 669 major cities face water shortages, of these 110 face serious water shortages. Climate change modelling shows that Northern China is going to get significantly drier leading to crop failure and desertification which is already happening in many places. Inner Mongolia has been particularly badly hit with ever drier conditions and creeping desertification. Near Dongsheng an area known as Hong Hai Zai used to be a large lake which finally dried up completely in 1999, leaving a baked landscape. This Mongolian man leads his camel across what was the former lake bed.

Above:
Near Dongsheng an area known as Hong Hai Zai used to be a large lake. Its waters used to harbour many fish, caught and sold at market by the locals. Here a pair of shoes lie abandoned amongst the left over saline deposits on the former lake bed.

Above:
An empty village reservoir in Shanxi
Province which has been particularly badly
hit by China's ongoing drought. Thousands
of people who used to be able to make a
living from the land, have had to abandon
their villages and migrate to the cities as
they can no longer grow crops.

Right:
Creeping desertification. Sand dunes
spreading across the highway in Inner
Mongolia, Northern China.

Above:
Withered crops dry up near Beijing, China. The ongoing drought is leading to water shortages and a significant drop in food production. Climate change is already negatively impacting on crop production in many areas of the world.

Above left:
A dust storm and desertification surrounds a wind farm in Inner Mongolia, China.

Below left:
A worker toiling in desiccated fields in Shanxi Province. Unless it rains any crops they are preparing the ground for are unlikely to grow.

Left:
Eucalyptus trees killed by the drought near Lake Eucumbene in New South Wales, Australia in February 2010. Much of Victoria and New South Wales have been gripped by an awful drought for the last 10 years, which has hugely impacted wildlife and agricultural productivity.

Above:
Where has all the water gone. Lake Hume is the largest reservoir in Australia and was set up to provide irrigation water for farms further down the Murray Basin and drinking water for Adelaide. On the day this photograph was taken it was at 19.6% capacity. By the end of the summer of 2009 it dropped to 2.1% capacity. Such impacts of the drought are likely to worsen as a result of climate change. The last time the water was anywhere near this road bridge was ten years ago, rendering this no fishing sign, somewhat redundant.

Above:
Red Gum trees are iconic Australian trees that grow along the banks of the Murray River. They rely on a regular flood cycle to survive. The unprecedented drought of the last 15 years has lead to low river levels on the Murray River. This and upstream dams taking water out for irrigation has vastly reduced the seasonal flooding. As a result 75% of the Red Gums are either dead, as these trees, or dying.

Right:
A farmer's watering hole on a farm near Shepperton, Australia.

Above:
A farmer's watering hole on a farm near Shepperton, Victoria, Australia, almost dried up. Victoria and New South Wales have been gripped by the worst drought in living memory for the last 15 years. River levels have dropped, water holes have dried up and stocking rates on many farms have dropped as the land can no longer support as many beasts.

Above left:
Even Kangaroos, a species well adapted to drought conditions are suffering.

Left:
A scientific experiment by scientists from Sydney University, in the Snowy Mountains. The study is monitoring CO_2 exchange between the atmosphere and the soil on a grassland plot.

Pages 140 - 141:
Forest ghosts. Lake Eildon, Victoria, Australia, was built in the 1950's to provide irrigation water, but the last time it was full was in 1995. The day the shot was taken it was at 29% capacity with levels down around 75 feet. The trees that were drowned and killed when the reservoir was first filled now stand well clear of the water.

Adjacent page,top left:
The dried up river bed of the Kern River in Bakersfield, California, USA.

Adjacent page,top right:
A horse in a drought parched landscape in Bakersfield, California, USA. Following the four year long drought, Bakersfield is now the driest city in the USA.

Adjacent page bottom left:
Drought parched ranch land near Bakersfield, California.

Adjacent page bottom right:
A farmers sign about the water crisis near Bakersfield in the Central Valley, California, USA, with the soil turned to dust. The whole of California is in a catastrophic drought with $2 Billion annually lost from the agricultural sector.

Left:
Drought killed trees near Tehachapi Pass, in California.

Above:
Lake Isabella near Bakersfield, is at less than 13% capacity. The boat launching jetty has been taken as far down the ramp as possible, and is still nowhere near the water level.

Right:
The upper part of Lake Isabella has nearly completely disappeared.

Far left:
A Golden Eagle that has taken an American Coot at Lake Success near Porterville. The lake is at 7% capacity. Most of California is in exceptional drought, the highest level of drought classification. This magnificent predator is sat on a tree stump that would normally be 50 feet underwater.

Top left:
The Kern Valley Wildlife Refuge in California's Central Valley was created as important resting and feeding grounds for wildfowl migrating along the Pacific flyway. After four years of unprecedented drought, the water shortages in California are critical. The reserve has received only 40% of its usual water, with the result that most of the lake beds are dried up and desiccated, leaving the birds nowhere to go.

Below left:
Looking down from Moro Rock in the Sequoia National Park California, USA, into the Central Valley, with dust from the drought illuminated by the setting sun.

Right:
A dairy farm in California's Central Valley, which in September 2015 was in the grip of a four year long drought. Unusustainable doesn't even begin to describe the damage done to the climate and the environment by the livestock industry.

Below right:
Sea of Sand. The Mesquite flat sand dunes in Death Valley.

Far right:
Visions of the future. The Mesquite flat sand dunes in Death Valley.

Left:
Abandoned dead and dying Orange trees that no longer have water to irrigate them near Delano.

Above:
Vincent Felix a farm worker oversees almond groves being chopped down in Wasco in the Central Valley of California. Following the four year long drought, there is no longer water available to irrigate them. 80% of the world's almonds are grown in California, and it takes 1.1 gallons of water to grow each nut. Many farms have run out of water, and $2.2 Billion has been wiped off the agriculture sector annually.

Above:
Dying grape vines in Bakersfield, California, USA that no longer have the water to irrigate them. 428,000 acres of agricultural land have been taken out of production due to lack of water. Thousands of agricultural workers have lost their jobs and one third of all children in California go to bed hungry, directly as a result of the catastrophic drought.

Above:
Water is life. Women come to collect water from a water charity in Porterville, California supplying bottled water to houses who have had no running water for over five months.

Right:
A war veteran collects water from a charity in Porterville. Houses in the East of Porterville, many of which are on private wells, have run completely out of water as the water table has dropped catastrophically.

Left:
A woman with a bottle of water next to a wall covered in traditional murals in La Paz, Bolivia. La Paz is desperately short of water as the glaciers on the surrounding Andean peaks are receding rapidly.

Above:
Maria Martinez fills a bucket from a tank outside her house supplied by a water charity in Porterville. Maria's house has had no running water for over five months.

Following page:
La Paz, Bolivia the world's highest capital city. It will probably be the first capital city in the world that will have to be largely abandoned due to lack of water. It relies heavily on glacial meltwater from the surrounding Andean peaks, but as climate change causes the glaciers to melt, it is rapidly running short of water.

153

Previous page:
Colourful lakes below the peak of
Chacaltaya in the Bolivian Andes, with a
reservoir discoloured by mine effluent that
is running low on water.

Above:
Laguna Miluni at a low level, with Lama's
grazing on the Altiplano in the background.

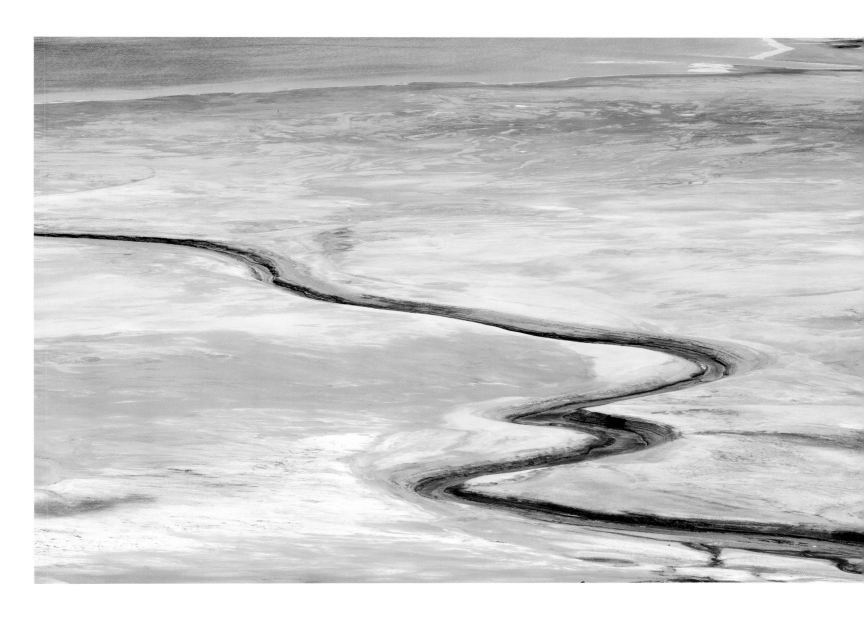

Above:
Laguna Miluni is a reservoir fed by
glacial meltwater from the Andean peak
of Huayna Potosi in the Bolivian Andes.
As the glaciers melt, the water supply for
La Paz, Bolivia's capital city is rapidly
running dry. The reservoir is also
contaminated by mine effluent as well as
being at a low level due to the drought.

Above:
The dam of Laguna Miluni showing how
low the reservoir has become.

Above:
Laguna Miluni at a low level looking
towards Chacaltaya, whose glacier has
now completely melted.

Adjacent page, top:
A house belonging to Allan Lehepuu in the mountains near Michelago, New South Wales, that was destroyed by bush fires in December 2009. Allan is a volunteer fire fighter and selflessly went to help fight the fire at the bottom of the mountain. The fire spread rapidly and destroyed Allan's and other houses in the area.

Adjacent page, bottom:
A roadside fire near Shepperton, Victoria, Australia, likely started by a motorist throwing a cigarette out of the window.

Above left:
Smoke from bush fires over a dawn landscape near Orbost, New South Wales, Australia.

Below left:
Forest fires are becoming more frequent as rising temperatures and drier weather in many areas of the world provides ideal conditions for combustion. Here smoke envelopes Black Spruce forest North of Fairbanks in Alaska. Summer 2004 was particularly hot in Alaska leading to an area of forest the size of the British Isles being scorched. As well as being a disaster for wildlife, the burning trees release vast stored quantities of carbon dioxide. One of many examples of feedback loops which are pushing climate change beyond human control.

Left:
Burnt vehicle at Kinglake which was one of the worst affected communities of the catastrophic 2009 Australian Bush Fires in the state of Victoria. 173 people were killed and many more left injured and traumatised, with 7,000 left homeless. The fires followed a period of prolonged drought and extreme high temperatures, when the thermometer on Black Saturday topped out at 47 degrees centigrade.

Above:
Rebuilding at Marysville which was one of the worst affected communities of the catastrophic 2009 Australian Bush Fires in the state of Victoria. 173 people were killed and many more left injured and traumatised.

Above:
Grazi Lisciotto and friend who were horribly burned in
house fires. They now work for the Peter Hughes Burns
Foundation in Australia providing counselling and
support for the victims of the bush fires.

Above:
A swimming pool on a burnt out house plot in Marysville
which was one of the worst affected communities of the
catastrophic 2009 Australian Bush Fires in the state
of Victoria.

Left and above:
Forest destroyed by bush fires near
Michelago, New South Wales, Australia,
in December 2009.

Adjacent page:
Meadow Pipit chicks killed by the fire.

Above left:
Following the warmest and driest April on record, moorland fires broke out across the UK. Ogden Moor near Wainstalls above Halifax was one of many fires. Several square Km of moorland burned for four days. The blaze was tackled by fire fighters, but despite their efforts the blaze destroyed valuable moorland habitat, killing mammals and amphibians and destroying birds nests.

Below left:
A moorland birds egg fried by fire. An unusually dry spring led to tinder dry conditions on moorland near Littleborough above Manchester, UK. A discarded cigarette probably set fire to the moor on the 25th of May. The flames, fanned by strong winds, destroyed over 300 acres of moorland. This upland habitat is home to many uncommon ground nesting birds including Curlew, Golden Plover and Twite. Many nests were destroyed.

Above:
A fire fighter covering his face against the smoke whilst tackling the Ogden Moor fire above Halifax, UK.

Right:
Smoke shrouds the forest from the King Fire that burned 97,717 acres of the El Dorado National Forest in California, USA.

Bottom right:
A sign for the appropriately named Hell Hole in the King Fire.

Adjacent page, top:
The King Fire in the El Dorado National Forest, California, USA. Following an unprecedented four year long drought, wild fires are much more common. Most of California is in exceptional drought, the highest level of drought classification. The fires release massive amounts of CO_2 into the atmosphere, one of many feedback loops exacerbating climate change.

Adjacent page, bottom left:
A Sky Crane helicopter that was used to tackle the King Fire in California, USA.

Adjacent page, bottom right:
An exhausted fire fighter in the middle of a 14 hour shift, tackling the King Fire.

Above:
Foscheck fire retardant dropped on a wild
fire near Hawkins Peak above Coleville
in the Great Central Divide Mountains,
California, USA.

Right:
A fire destroys an area of forest in the
Little Yosemite Valley in the Yosemite
National Park, California, USA. This fire
was started by a lightning strike.

Left:
The heart that has been ripped out of the forest. A fire destroys an area of forest in the Little Yosemite Valley in the Yosemite National Park.

Above:
Boreal Forest burnt and a forest fire raging on Octopus Mountain in Kootenay National Park, Canada.

Shishmaref

I met Raymond Weyiouanna (pictured right) in 2004 on my first dedicated climate change photo shoot. He is considered by many to be the world's first refugee from climate change after his house was washed into the sea in 1998. For the Inuit residents of Shishmaref, a tiny island between Alaska and Siberia, climate change is very real and has been impacting them for decades. Sea ice that used to envelop the island around late September is now not forming until December. This leaves the island vulnerable to storms that have already washed 10 houses into the sea, leading to them being referred to as the world's first refugees from climate change. Other houses have had to be moved back from the edge. The animals they rely on as part of their subsistence culture are becoming harder to find, as they migrate further north, away from the island. It was a real privilege to spend time with people who still live so close to the land and nature. Shishmaref's residents hunt Caribou and Seal, fish for Salmon in the Fall and pick berries on the tundra. Their carbon footprint is tiny compared to most western folk. I was for the first time to realise something I have witnessed many times since, that is, those that are least responsible for climate change are most severely impacted by it.

As this book was going to print, the residents of Shishmaref took the unprecedented and historic step of voting to leave their island home. The whole village now needs to be relocated to an as yet unidentified site on the mainland, less vulnerable to sea level rise and storm surge erosion, at an estimated cost of $180 million.

Left:
Inuit hunter gatherers on Shishmaref a tiny island between Alaska and Siberia in the Chukchi sea which is home to around 600 Inuits. As hunter gatherers their carbon footprint is tiny and as such are least responsible for climate change.

Above:
Salmon caught by Inuits on Shishmaref, Alaska.

Above:
Pacific Salmon drying on racks on
Shishmaref to be stored for winter food.

Adjacent page:
A woman skins a Spotted Seal on
Shishmaref, every part of the animal will
be used, skin for clothing, meat for food
and offal to feed the sled dogs.

Above:
Gone but not forgotten. J J Weyouanna's
wife stands on the beach where their
house used to stand on Shishmaref, a tiny
island between Alaska and Siberia.

Above:
The remains of an Inuits house on
Shishmaref that was washed into the sea
by a winter storm before the sea ice
had formed.

Above:
Inuit houses on Shishmaref perilously
close to the edge, following coastal
erosion which has accelerated due to lack
of sea ice for protection.

Above:
An Inuit summer hunting camp at the
mouth of the Serpentine river near
Shishmaref, Alaska.

Left:
Inuit women wearing traditional national costume, or Kalaallisuut, in Ilulissat on Greenland. The costume consists of seal skin boots (Unnaat) bead necklaces (Nuilaqutit) and seal-skin trousers (Takisut).

Above:
An Inuit man with traditional Eskimo art on Shishmaref. A culture much threatened by climate change.

Glacial retreat and permafrost melt

There are fewer more obvious signs that the planet is warming than the rapid retreat of glaciers. In my own lifetime I have witnessed glaciers in the European Alps retreat massively, leaving huge scars on the land, where bare rock was once buried deep beneath ice. There is barely a glacier on the planet that is not receding, some have already completely disappeared. These important reservoirs of water are a critical life support system for millions of people who rely on the summer melt water for drinking and to irrigate their crops. Glaciers are either found towards the poles, or at high altitude. The polar regions have warmed much more rapidly than areas closer to the equator, with disastrous consequences for glacial regimes. To stand at the snout of a glacier and watch it calve huge chunks of ice, possibly hundreds of thousands of years old, is to witness the raw power of nature and the folly of our addiction to fossil fuels. One glacier alone shows some mind boggling statistics. I visited the Jakobshavn glacier on Greenland's West coast in 2008. The Jakobshavn glacier or Sermeq Kujalleq drains 7% of the Greenland ice sheet and is the largest glacier outside Antarctica. It calves enough ice in one day to supply New York with water for one year. It is one of the fastest moving glaciers in the world at up to 46 metres per day (19 metres per day before 2002) and has also receded rapidly (45 km since 1850) due to human induced climate change as temperatures have risen in Greenland by 9°F in the last 60 years. It calves around 35 billion tonnes of ice annually. In 2012 the glacier was witnessed calving a 7.4 cubic kilometre mass of ice, that was up to 800 feet high and was larger than the area of Manhattan.

Another worrying consequence of climate change in polar latitudes is the amount of methane locked up in the permafrost. Methane is some 23 times more potent than CO_2 as a greenhouse gas, and billions of tonnes of it are locked up in the permafrost. It is one of many examples of a feedback loop, where rising temperatures start to melt the permafrost, releasing methane, that accelerates the warming and melting, releasing yet more methane in an ever increasing spiral.

Right:
The Jacobshavn glacier. An underwater moraine
at the mouth of the fjord grounds the largest icebergs
causing a backlog of ice completely blocking the
entire length of the fjord with ice.

Above:
The Russell Glacier draining the Greenland ice sheet inland from Kangerlussuaq on Greenland's west coast. This glacier has speeded up in recent years and is also receding rapidly due to human induced climate change. Greenland has warmed nine degrees fahrenheit in the last 60 years.

Above:
Ice fallen from the snout of the Russell Glacier.

Far left:
Collapsing ice at the snout of the Russell Glacier draining the Greenland ice sheet.

Above left:
PhD scientist Ian Bartholomew using dye tracing techniques as part of a study to measure the speed of the Russell Glacier near Kangerlussuag, Greenland. The study is looking at how increasing quantities of melt water caused by climate change are affecting the glaciers' speed, which like most glaciers in Greenland has sped up considerably in the last 20 years. As part of the study reflective poles were drilled 4 metres into the ice to measure their speed at various positions on the glacier. Within a month all the poles had fallen over as the glacier melted down over 4 metres. The study conclusively showed that the speed of the glacier was directly linked to the amount of meltwater draining from its snout.

Below left:
Water samples taken from the meltwater river at the snout of the Russell Glacier near Kangerlussuaq.

Left:
Colourful houses in Ilulissat with icebergs in the bay.

Above right:
Fire extinguishers dumped on a tip at Kangerlussuag in Greenland, like a metaphor for a warming world. Can we put the fire out in time?

Below right:
Oil and ice. Oil barrels dumped on the tundra outside Ilulissat in Greenland with icebergs behind from the Illulissat Ice fjord. The Ilulissat ice fjord is a Unesco world heritage site.

Previous page:
Tourist boat trips sail through Icebergs at midnight from the Jacobshavn glacier.

Above and right:
Weird eroded shapes in Icebergs from the Jacobshavn glacier.

Adjacent page, top left:
Icebergs from the Jacobshavn glacier
choking the fjord.

Adjacent page, top right:
Icebergs from the Jacobshavn glacier.

Adjacent page, bottom:
Massive icebergs from the Jacobshavn
glacier.

Above:
Melt water drains off the Greenland
ice sheet.

Left:
A 20 ton ice explorer truck owned and
run by Arngrimur Hermannsson next to a
Moulin, or sink hole for meltwater.
He uses the truck to take tourists onto the
Langjokull ice cap. Like all Iceland's
glaciers it is melting rapidly and predicted
to disappear within 100 years. As Arni says,
every time I come up here, the glacier
has retreated a bit further.

Right:
Melt water lakes on the Greenland ice
sheet in West Greenland, from the air.
The ice sheet is up to 250,000 years old
and up to 3,200 metres thick. Climate
change is currently leading to rapid melt
of the ice sheet which if it were to melt
entirely would raise global sea levels by
seven metres, swamping most major cities
of the world and displacing hundreds of
millions of people.

Adjacent page - top left:
Melt water on the Greenland ice sheet
near camp Victor North of Ilulissat.
The Greenland ice sheet is the largest ice
sheet outside of Antarctica. The ice sheet
is melting at unprecedented rates,
deeply worrying as the ice sheet contains
enough water to raise global sea levels
by seven metres.

Adjacent page - top right:
Melt water on the Greenland ice sheet
and soot fallout from forest fires in Siberia.
The soot on the glacier increases the
melting rate as the darker layer absorbs
more of the suns energy.

Adjacent page - bottom:
Water drips from a melting Iceberg, from
the Jacobshavn glacier.

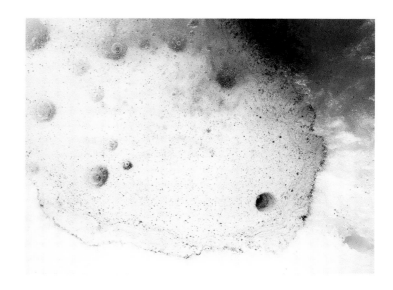

Above:
Tourists riding through a stinking fog of exhaust fumes from skidoos on the Langjokull ice sheet in Iceland. Like all of Iceland's glaciers it is retreating rapidly due to climate change.

Right:
Mountaineer Mike Withers peers into the depths of a huge crevasse on the Glacier Du Geant. Like all Alpine glaciers it is retreating rapidly.

Left:
The Glacier du Tour which retreated 200 metres between 2004 and 2012, Chamonix, France.

Above:
Climbers descend ladders leading down onto the Mer De Glace from near the Montenvers railway station. The railway was built in Victorian times to take tourists up to the glacier, it has subsequently thinned 150 meters since 1820, and retreated by 2,300 metres. In order to access the glacier you now have to climb down over 100 metres on ladders.

Following page:
A summer avalanche caused by serac collapse off a melting glacier on Mont Blanc, Chamonix, France.

Adjacent page,top left:
The author on the summit of the 4,248 metre peak of Mont Blanc Du Tacul above Chamonix, France.

Adjacent page,top right:
Climbers ascending the 4,248 metre peak of Mont Blanc du Tacul. Climate change is melting the permafrost that holds many Alpine peaks together making high altitude mountaineering more dangerous. This route to the summit that I climbed in 2007 is now rarely used as it has become too dangerous with increasing serac fall and avalanche.

Adjacent page bottom left:
Paraponters preparing to take off from a melting glacier on the Grand Montets above Chamonix.

Adjacent page bottom right:
The Gornergrat railway above Zermatt, Switzerland in front of the iconic Matterhorn whose glaciers are receding rapidly.

Left:
A mountain guide points out a rapidly retreating glacier on Mont Blanc to walkers on the Tour de Mont Blanc.

Far left:
Jill Cooper snow shoeing in the Urho Kehkkosen National Park near Saariselka, Northern Finland, looking into Russia. Winters are getting both warmer and wetter and in Southern Finland winters are becoming increasingly snow free.
Such iconic winter scenes could in a relatively short space of time become a thing of the past.

Above left:
The Athabasca glacier is receding extremely rapidly and has lost over 60% of its ice mass in less than 150 years. A sign marks where the glacier stood in 1908. The author wears a protest T shirt in the foreground.

Below Left:
Meltwater pools and tourist buggy on the Athabasca Glacier in the Canadian Rockies. It is receding extremely rapidly and has lost over 60% of its ice mass in less than 150 years.

Left:
Alpine Bearberry in front of the Harding Ice Field, Kenai Fjords National Park, Alaska. The ice sheet up to 5,000 feet thick in places is thinning rapidly due to warming temperatures.

Above:
An avalanche on Machapuchare or Fishtail Peak in the Annapurna Himalaya, Nepal. It was caused by a massive block of glacial ice detaching from the summit cliffs of this 6,993 metre tall peak on 29th December 2012. Such ice avalanches are more common in Spring and Summer, as in Winter, the ice is normally frozen and more stable. The avalanche descended around 12,000 feet, and covered trekkers on the valley path below in snow.

Pages 220 - 221:
Alpenglow at sunrise on Annapurna South and Annapurna Fang, Nepalese Himalayas.

Pages 222 - 223:
A warming world. Alpenglow at sunset on Machapuchare, Annapurna Sanctuary, Nepalese Himalayas.

Pages 224 - 225:
Prayer flags at Annapurna Sanctuary and base camp at 4,130 metres looking towards Machapuchare. Even on the highest mountains on the planet, glaciers are receding rapidly.

Above:
The rapidly retreating South Annapurna glacier in the Annapurna Sanctuary, Nepalese Himalayas. The retreating glacier has left a huge empty chasm that until recent times was filled with ice. All of the Himalaya's glaciers are retreating rapidly. The glaciers feed many of Asia's largest rivers that billions of people rely on for water. As these reservoirs disappear, it will have disastrous consequences for water supplies.

Right:
Above the emptying trough of the rapidly receding South Annapurna glacier, stands a memorial to Mario Merelli, an Italian climber killed on Annapurna.

Mario Merelli was a superb italian mountaineer with a great heart towards others who were in need, especially towards the children in the most remote areas of the Himalayas. He is still with us on these mountains in the heights looking down on us all. Goodbye (Ciao) Mario.

Your friends
30.09.2012

Left:
The old ski club hut on the peak of
Chacaltaya (5,395 metres), until 2009
Chacaltaya had a glacier which supported
the worlds highest ski lift at over 17,000
feet. The glacier finally disappeared
completely in 2009.

Above:
The switchback road that climbs to over
17,000 feet to the peak of Chacaltaya,
above La Paz, Bolivia. It is one of the
highest roads in the world. The Chacaltaya
glacier used to support the world's highest
ski resort until the glacier which had been
receding for years, finally disappeared
in 2009.

Above right:
Adolfo Mendoza used to look after Chacaltaya's ski hut and still climbs the peak every day to open up the hut to tourists. The slope in the background is where the Chacaltaya glacier used to be upon which the skiing took place. Now all that is left are a few snow patches.

Below right
An indigenous woman selling traditional colourful Bolivian fabric at a street market in El Alto, Bolivia, with the peak of Illimani in the background. El Alto is running critically short of water, as it relies on the surrounding Andean peaks for glacial meltwater. As the glaciers recede the city is increasingly short of water.

Above: left
Early melt causing collapsing ice structures at the ice palace built with blocks from the Songhue river in Harbin, Heilongjiang Province, Northern China. It is part of the annual Harbin ice festival that attracts up to five million visitors a year. Huge ice sculptures are disappearing before the tourists that flock to the festival get to see them. The average temperature of Winter in Harbin is 5°C higher than historical records, posing a real threat to the festival that hugely benefits the local economy.

Below left:
Ice breaking up in Spring on the Yellow River in Northern China. From 1968 to 2001, the freeze duration has shortened significantly by 38 days at Bayangaole and 25 days at Sanhuhe, respectively. The flow rate has reduced from 500 to 260 m3 s−1, and the expanse of river freeze has also decreased significantly by about 310 km. In the lower reach of the river, the location of earliest ice breakup has shifted downstream significantly in the last 50 years.

Above:
Ice strengthened for expedition cruising, the Akedimk Sergey Vavilov
sits in rotten sea ice off northern Svalbard, above 80N, some 550 miles
from the North Pole. The Arctic has lost 40% of its sea ice cover since
1980 and 75% of its volume. Scientists believe the North Pole could be
entirely ice-free in Summer by the middle of this century, if not earlier.

Above:
Rotten sea ice at over 80 degrees off the North of Svalbard.
Climate change is causing sea ice to retreat rapidly.

Above:
Blue Berg. An iceberg from a glacier in Northern Svalbard. All of Svalbard's glaciers are retreating, even in the north of the archipelago despite only being around 600 miles from the North Pole.

Above:
Black Legged Kittiwake (Rissa tridactyla) and Northern Fulmar
(Fulmarus glacialis) flee from a large calving of ice off the face of a
glacier in Northern Svalbard in the high Arctic.

Left:
A Polar Bear hunting seals on rotten sea ice off the north coast of Spitsbergen, only 500 nautical miles from the North Pole. Climate change poses a huge threat to Polar Bears. As the sea ice retreats, they lose ground and time to hunt their main prey, seals, which they can only hunt on sea ice. Latest research shows that the Arctic will be free of Summer sea ice by the 2050's and Polar Bears are likely to become extinct in the wild.

Above:

A male Polar Bear (Ursus maritimus) that starved to death as a consequence of climate change. This male Polar Bear was last tracked by the Norwegian Polar Institute in April 2013 in southern Svalbard. Polar Bears need sea ice to hunt their main prey, seals. Western fjords of Svalbard which normally freeze in winter, remained ice free all season during the Winter of 2012 /13, one of the worst on record for sea ice around the island archipelago. This bear headed hundreds of miles north, looking for suitable sea ice to hunt on, finding no suitable sea ice, finally exhausted, it collapsed and died. The future for Polar Bear looks bleak in a climate changing world. Recent scientific studies show that Polar Bear are getting thinner and weighing less due primarily to less time to hunt in the winter and a longer fasting period in summer. Without sea ice, they will no doubt all starve to death.

Left:
At the other end of the planet, an ice strengthened ship, the Akademik Sergey Vavilov, on an expedition cruise to Antarctica. It sits off the Antarctic Peninsular at the Gerlache Strait, in melting sea ice. The Antarctic Peninsular is one of the most rapidly warming places on the planet.

Top right:
Catherine Johnstone-Brooks and Rus Margolin show unbridled joy amongst the pristine splendour that is Antarctica, Joinville Island just off the Antarctic Peninsular.

Bottom right:
Rus Margolin and a whale vertebrae on Curverville Island, Antarctic Peninsular, with melting icebergs.

237

Previous page:
Pristine. Members of an expedition cruise
to Antarctica aboard a Zodiak, Fournier
Bay, Gerlache Strait on the Antarctic
Peninsular travelling through melting
sea ice.

Above left:
Though pristine looking, these glaciers in
the Gerlache Strait, separating the Palmer
Archipelago from the Antarctic Peninsular
off Anvers Island, are retreating.

Below right:
Stunning coastal scenery and a receding
glacier beneath Mount Walker in Paradise
Bay off Graham Land on the Antarctic
Peninsular.

Adjacent page:
The Griffin. A fantastic bird shaped
iceberg amongst stunning coastal scenery
beneath Mount Walker in Paradise Bay off
Graham Land on the Antarctic Peninsular.

Above:
A Leopard Seal (Hydrurga leptonyx) hauled out on an iceberg in the Drygalski Fjord, Antarctic Peninsular. A 6C rise in temperatures in the last half century has caused the disappearance of large areas of sea ice on which the seals breed.

Above:

Crabeater Seal (Lobodon carcinophaga) on an iceberg in Paradise
Bay, Antarctica. Crabeater Seals are the most common large mammal
on the planet after humans, with an estimated population of 15 million.
They are a true Antarctic species, living on or around sea ice; as the
sea ice retreats they are at real risk. Their main diet is Krill, numbers
of which have reduced by over 50%. Antarctic Krill feed on algae which
grow on the underside of sea ice, as the sea ice retreats, the algae is
less common, ergo less food for Krill, less Crabeater Seals.

Far left:
Ice spire. Antarctic glacial scenery on the Antarctic Peninsular near Anvers Island.

Left:
A mountaineer winter climbing in Coire an Sneachda in the Cairngorm mountains of Scotland. Rapid rises in winter temperature can lead to great instability in the snowpack and ice, making this an even more dangerous activity than normal.

Above:
Icebergs streaming off the Greenland ice sheet in East Greenland. All this fresh water that has been locked up as ice for hundreds of thousands of years is contributing to sea level rise.

Left:
An old house at Recherchefjorden (77°31'N 14°36'E), Van Keulenfjorden, Spitsbergen, Svalbard gradually sliding down slope due to solifluction and permafrost melt. Climate change is accelerating permafrost melt and causing huge damage across the Arctic. It is also one of the feedback loops that exacerbate climate change. Permafrost locks away billions of tonnes of methane (a greenhouse gas 23 times more potent than CO_2), as the permafrost melts this methane is released into the atmosphere with potentially disastrous consequences.

Top right:
A house on the appropriately named Madcap Lane in Fairbanks, Alaska collapsing into the ground due to permafrost melt.

Bottom right:
A desperate householder uses a jack to try and keep their house level as it sinks into the ground due to permafrost melt, Fairbanks, Alaska. Image taken in 2004.

Above:
A house collapsed into a hole in the ground as the permafrost beneath it melts. Fairbanks, Alaska, taken in 2004.

Above:
Drunken Forest in Fairbanks Alaska, a phenomenon caused by
permafrost melt. The Boreal forest faces an uncertain future, collapsing
due to permafrost melt, killed by Spruce Bark Beetles spreading ever
further northwards in ever warming conditions and burnt to a cinder by
increasingly common forest fires.

Sea level rise

The earth's ice sheets and glaciers are a huge store of fresh water, a store that is rapidly diminishing, with the result that all this newly melted water is heading to the oceans and driving up sea level rise. The Greenland ice sheet alone contains enough ice to raise global sea levels by seven metres. Hundreds of millions of people around the globe live within five metres of sea level, many are starting to feel the impact. Tuvalu is the smallest nation in the world and will probably be the first country to disappear completely due to climate change. I visited this tiny island nation in the Pacific Ocean in 2007 to witness for myself the impact of the highest tides of the year. All the islands are coral atolls, which are low lying and very vulnerable to sea level rise. Being composed of coral, they are also porous, which means as the tides rise, water is forced up through the coral, to flood inner parts of Funafuti, the main inhabited island. More people climb Everest every year, than visit Funafuti, and out of sight can feel out of mind. What I witnessed was truly shocking. With a flat calm sea, at high tide, the middle of the island was up to four feet underwater. With every passing year, the levels creep higher and higher. The levels are now so high that one powerful cyclone, combined with a high tide, could destroy the island completely. Some of the residents have already been evacuated to New Zealand, the ones left behind face an increasingly uncertain future.

New York was recently inundated by a powerful storm that caused coastal flooding of many of its streets, shutting down the city and causing $billions of damage. We can not build our way out of sea level rise, in the coming years we will see a mass displacement of millions of people, that will make Hurricane Katrina that devastated New Orleans seem minor by comparison.

Right:
A collapsed coastal road between Skipsea and Ulrome on Yorkshire's East Coast, UK. The coast is composed of soft boulder clays, very vulnerable to coastal erosion. This section of coast has been eroding since Roman times, with many villages having disappeared into the sea, and is the fastest eroding coast in Europe. Climate change is speeding up the erosion, with sea level rise, increased stormy weather and increased heavy rainfall events, all playing their part.

Far left, top:
The tropical paradise of Tuvalu with fisherman on an island off Funafuti. These low lying islands are rapidly being eroded and washed away by rising sea levels. Satellite altimeters show that the seas around these vulnerable coral atoll islands are rising by 5mm a year. Tuvalu may well be the first nation on earth to be lost to climate change. Already some residents have moved to New Zealand, as ever increasing flooding events make life on the low lying islands difficult.

Far left, bottom:
A Tuvaluan mother and daughter on Funafuti, Tuvalu.

Above left:
A child dives into the sea at sunset on Funafuti, Tuvalu. The sea is their home and while it provides much of their food in the form of fish it also threatens to swamp their low-lying island home.

Below left:
A Tuvaluan man shelters on a hammock in the shade during the heat of the day, Funafuti Atoll, Tuvalu.

Following page:
The sheltered side of Tepuka island off Tuvalu.

Above:
Paradise Lost. On the other, seaward side of Tepuka island ever rising seas and stormy weather is undercutting the shore causing the trees to collapse onto the beach. The soils are then washed away, further eroding the island.

Above:
Trees knocked down by undercutting coastal erosion litter the beach
on Tepuka island off Funafuti atoll in Tuvalu.

Adjacent page, top:
Old vehicles being used in a desperate attempt to protect Funafuti's shoreline from coastal erosion and an ever increasing sea level, Tuvalu.

Adjacent page, bottom:
A Tuvaluan fisherman looks onto the destroyed island of Tepukasavilivili part of the Funafuti atoll. In 1997 cyclone Meli, ripped off its trees and most of its soil, leaving a coral stump, which is barely visible at high tide. Tepukasavilivili shows what the future holds for Tuvalu.

Top left:
Tuvaluans watch helplessly as the sea breaks over their island home, Funafuti, Tuvalu. The king tides are now so high, they swamp most of the islands, even when the sea is flat calm.

Bottom left:
Approaching Tepukasavilivili island off Funafuti, Tuvalu completely destroyed by cyclones and sea level rise.

Adjacent page, top:
Tuvaluans watch helplessly as the high tide inundates their island home on Funafuti, washing from one side of the island to the other.

Adjacent page, bottom left:
A pig flooded out on Funafuti Atoll, Tuvalu, during a king tide, showing how vulnerable this small island chain is to sea level rise.

Adjacent page, bottom right:
The eyes have it. A young Tuvaluan boy faces an uncertain future on Funafuti Atoll as sea level rise threatens their island home.

Top left:
A Tuvaluan child uses the flood waters to surf on an old fridge door, blissfully unaware of the threats to his future, Funafuti, Tuvalu.

Bottom left:
Children flee the rising floodwaters on Funafuti during one of the highest tides of the year. Despite it being a flat calm sea, the rising tide forced sea water up through the porous coral, flooding the centre of the island with up to four feet of water.

Left:
A healthy looking coral reef off Funafuti atoll, Tuvalu.
Warming oceans are increasingly leading to coral
bleaching. This is where the coral is stressed by the
warmer temperatures resulting in it ejecting the
algae, which give the coral its colour.

Above:
Coral on the Great Barrier Reef in Queensland,
Australia showing signs of coral bleaching.

Top right:
A woman sunbathing in front of hotels and apartment blocks on Miami Beach. The Florida coastline is highly developed and low lying making it very vulnerable to sea level rise.

Bottom right:
Royal Terns with hotels and apartment blocks on Miami Beach, Florida. The Florida coastline is extremely vulnerable to sea level rise, threatening both important wildlife habitat and real estate.

Adjacent page, top:
A sign about not walking on the small sand dunes that are all that stand in the way between the Atlantic Ocean and $Billions of real estate on Miami Beach, Florida, USA.

Adjacent page, bottom left:
Ocean Rescue, Miami Beach, Florida. It may not be long before the whole of Miami needs rescuing from the ever rising ocean.

Adjacent page, bottom right:
Workers creating a new beach resort on the Palm development in Dubai. Creating new sea front real estate is a questionable thing to do as sea level rise could well threaten it in the near future.

Above:
A Second world War Pill box on the beach near Aldbrough on Yorkshire's East Coast, UK. It was originally constructed on the cliff tops but has collapsed into the sea as the coastline rapidly erodes.

Above:
A Second World War lookout post leaning alarmingly and about
to tumble over the edge of the cliff near Aldbrough on Yorkshire's
East Coast, UK.

Far left:
Salt marsh at sunset in Cley next the Sea, North Norfolk, UK. This low lying coast is increasingly vulnerable to coastal flooding.

Left, top and bottom:
Before and after; showing coastal erosion at Happisburgh, Norfolk, UK.
The first shot (top) taken in 2010, shows the steps leading to the beach.
The second shot taken in 2015, shows the two concrete blocks that were the foundations for the steps, all that is left, after rapid coastal erosion.

Left:
The Breach at Alkborough on the Humber Estuary in Eastern England. As sea levels rise around the world many areas of low lying land are at increasing risk of coastal flooding and are getting increasingly expensive to protect. In order to protect nearby urban areas coastal realignment or managed retreat is now being used to take the pressure off during increasingly common storm surges. At Alkborough a 20 metre wide breach has been created in the sea defences to allow sea water to flood into former agricultural land, creating 150 hectares of wetland. As well as protecting nearby urban areas from flooding the site also provides valuable wetland habitat for wildlife. In 2008 Alkborough was the largest coastal realignment project in Europe and was quickly colonised by wildlife.

Above
Looking down onto high tide flooding at the Alkborough breach.

Left and above:
Kayakers and a stranded motorist in
the flood waters on the road at Storth on
the Kent Estuary in Cumbria, UK, during
the January 2014 storm surge and
high tides.

Following page:
Bamboo and mud coastal flood defences
in the Sunderbans, a low lying area of the
Ganges Delta, India, that is vulnerable to
sea level rise.

Adjacent page, top left:
The Netherlands are notoriously flat and low lying, with 50% of the country lying below sea level. Climate change is leading to both sea level rise and increased flooding, both of which threaten properties. One solution is to build floating houses, that rise and fall with altering water levels. Ijburg, a suburb of Amsterdam is the floating house capital, with increasing numbers of floating houses being constructed.

Adjacent page, top right:
The tethering system that allows a floating house to move up and down, and prevents them from floating away. Ijburg, Amsterdam, Netherlands.

Adjacent page, bottom:
Hinke Patist and her son outside their floating house in Ijburg, Amsterdam.

Left:
A floating house and its reflection in Ijburg, Amsterdam.

Impacted fauna and flora

All life on the planet is superbly adapted to specific conditions, be that altitude, temperature, weather etc. As conditions warm, so plants and animals start to respond to changing conditions. With greater stresses being placed on many species. Great Tits a small passerine found across much of Western Europe have been found to be nesting up to 14 days earlier than they did 40 years ago. All birds time their nesting, so that there is a ready available food supply to feed their young on. In the case of the Great Tit, that is linked to the emergence of woodland caterpillars. As the breeding cycle starts to become out of sync with the caterpillar cycle, they find it increasingly difficult to feed their young.

Studies on Alpine flora have shown that species of flowering plant are migrating to higher altitudes to find the conditions that they are adapted to. Obviously they can only migrate so far before they run out of options. Penguins in the Antarctic are reducing in numbers as the food they rely on declines, or in the case of the Adelie Penguin, the nesting conditions they prefer, alter. In the USA, Black Bears have been emerging from hibernation earlier, due to the earlier arrival of Spring. In the Arctic Caribou numbers are declining, as warming temperatures lead to layers of ice in the snow pack, that prevent them from accessing their food. Studies have shown that fewer calves are born following a warm Winter than a cold one. The list is endless, there can be few species that have been studied that are not impacted in some way, mostly negatively, by climate change.

Right:
A young King Penguin (Aptenodytes patagonicus)
moulting from its juvenile down to adult feathers at Gold
Harbour, South Georgia, Southern Ocean.

Right:
Blue Green algae on the shores of Lake Windermere in the Lake District, UK. Algal blooms are becoming far more frequent as temperatures rise.

Adjacent page, top left:
Black spruce trees killed by Spruce Bark Beetles spreading northwards as Winter temperatures soar in Alaska. Spruce Bark Beetles were never able to survive the Alaskan winters in large numbers, but as the temperatures have risen, more and more beetles survive, their numbers have proliferated, killing millions of acres of forest. Another example of a feedback loop which sees Boreal forest being pushed from a carbon sink, to a net contributor of carbon.

Adjacent page, top right:
A Common Frog (Rana temporaria) in my garden pond, UK. Records show that as Spring arrives earlier and earlier as the climate warms, that frogs are laying their spawn several weeks earlier than sixty years ago.

Adjacent page, bottom:
The Abbey Gardens on Tresco, in the Scilly Isles, off South West Cornwall, UK, renowned for its tropical plants which are able to grow due to the Gulf Stream, or North Atlantic Drift. This is a warm ocean current which keeps the islands warmer than they would otherwise be for their latitude, and also frost free. Scientists have already recorded a slowing down of the Gulf Stream caused by climate change. As cold fresh water pours off the arctic ice sheets, it prevents the denser salty water from sinking, which is the start of the conveyor. If you travel to the same latitude in Canada, you would find Polar Bears.

Above:
Whooper Swans (Cygnus cygnus) at Martin Mere bird reserve near Ormskirk, Lancashire, UK. Traditionally the UK provided a safe Winter refuge for migratory wildfowl which flew over from the continent to escape freezing conditions. As temperatures soar, fewer numbers of ducks and swans need to make the hazardous journey, as they can find suitable conditions to overwinter closer to their breeding grounds.

Right:
A Great Tit (Parus major) nesting in a garden pot in the UK. The UK has the longest nest record scheme in the world run by the British Trust for Ornithology. Its records show that Great Tits are now nesting up to 14 days earlier in Spring due to climate change.

Adjacent page, top:
Walrus (Odobenus rosmarus) off a beach in northern Svalbard, once hunted to near extinction they are now recovering, only to be affected by climate change which reduces the sea ice they like to haul out on to rest between bouts of feeding.

Adjacent page, bottom:
Little Auks or Dovekie (Alle alle) at a nesting colony at Sallyhamna (79°51'N 11°23'E) on the north coast of Svalbard. These small Auks are specialist Arctic birds and only nest in the far north. Research has shown they are having to travel further to find suitable feeding conditions.

Left:
A pair of Black Browed Albatross (Thalassarche melanophris) allopreening to reinforce the pair bond in a nesting colony on Westpoint Island in the Falkland Islands off Argentina. Albatrosses are globally threatened by long line fishing boats who are responsible for killing thousands of birds. They are being watched by Rockhopper Penguins (Eudyptes chrysocome) in the background. Both species are negatively impacted by climate change, which is altering the range of their favoured prey species.

Above:
King Penguins (Aptenodytes patagonicus) emerge from a fishing trip out to sea onto the beach in the world's second largest King Penguin colony on Salisbury Plain, South Georgia, Southern Ocean. King Penguins feed mainly on Krill, numbers of which have crashed in recent years, causing a drop in King Penguin numbers. Krill feed on algae that grows on the underside of sea ice. As the sea ice retreats there is less algae, less krill and fewer King Penguins.

Right:
A King Penguin on Salisbury Plain, South Georgia, with passengers from an expedition cruise.

Far left:
Gentoo Penguins (Pygoscelis papua) amongst stunning coastal scenery in Paradise Bay off Graham Land on the Antarctic Peninsular. The Peninsular is one of the most rapidly warming places on the planet. As the Antarctic Peninsular warms, Gentoo's are moving into areas once only the preserve of the Adelie Penguin.

Left:
An Adelie Penguin (Pygoscelis adeliae) at Madder Cliffs, Suspiros Bay, at the west end of Joinville Island, Antarctica. Adelie's are a true Antarctic species which are suffering as a result of climate change. The Antarctic Peninsular, their only breeding grounds, is one of the fastest warming areas on the planet. This is causing Adelies to migrate south. They are reducing in numbers, they feed almost exclusively on Krill, which is also declining as a result of climate change.

Above:
A Humpback Whale (Megaptera novaeangliae) feeding on Krill in Wilhelmena Bay, Antarctic Peninsular. The whales migrate here in the Summer to feed. Krill numbers have declined by over 50%. Krill feed on algae that grows on the underside of sea ice. As the sea ice melts, both algae and Krill decline.

Forests

The forests of the world are the lungs of the planet. They are crucial for biodiversity, for releasing the oxygen that we breath, and for sequestrating the CO_2 that we release. We continue to deforest the planet at an alarming rate, just at the very time that increased forest cover could help us tackle climate change. Much has been made of the rates of deforestation of the Amazon rain forest, the world's greatest forest. New research has revealed that the rainforest generates its own rain, but that cycle is being interrupted by increasing incidence of drought across Amazonia. This is starting to kill off the forest, almost as fast as man is chopping it down and clearing it for agriculture. The fertility of rainforest soils is maintained by the rainforest itself. Once the forest is removed, the soils lose their fertility rapidly, leaving farmers with no option but to apply increasingly expensive applications of fertiliser. Deforestation also leaves the soil vulnerable to erosion. Heavy rainfall events are washing increasingly large areas of the precious soil away.

By chopping down the world's great forests, we are losing species potentially useful for humanity, before we even have a chance to identify them.

Right:
Rainforests around the world hold some of the greatest biodiversity of species on the planet. They are responsible for controlling the weather in some cases and are an important carbon sink. Much has been made of deforestation of this vital resource, but in many areas climate change is leading to drier less suitable conditions for the tropical vegetation to grow. This forest is in Fiji.

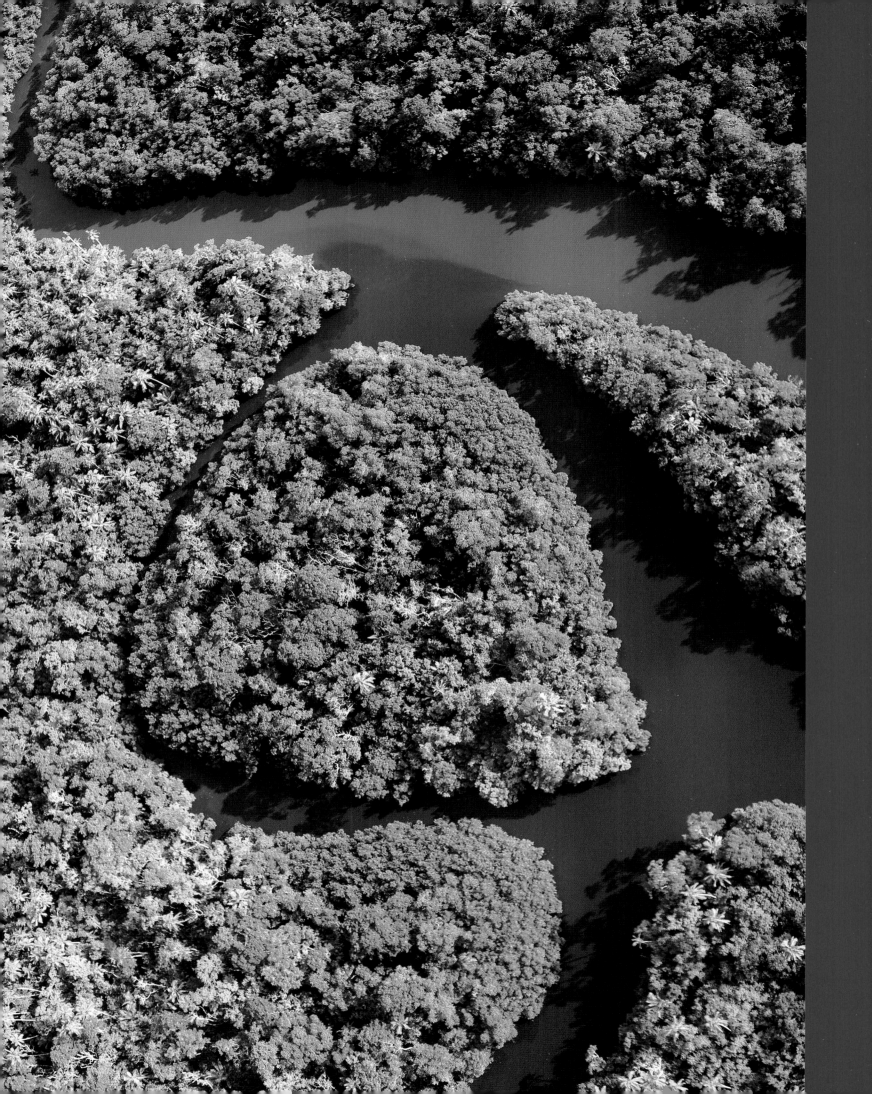

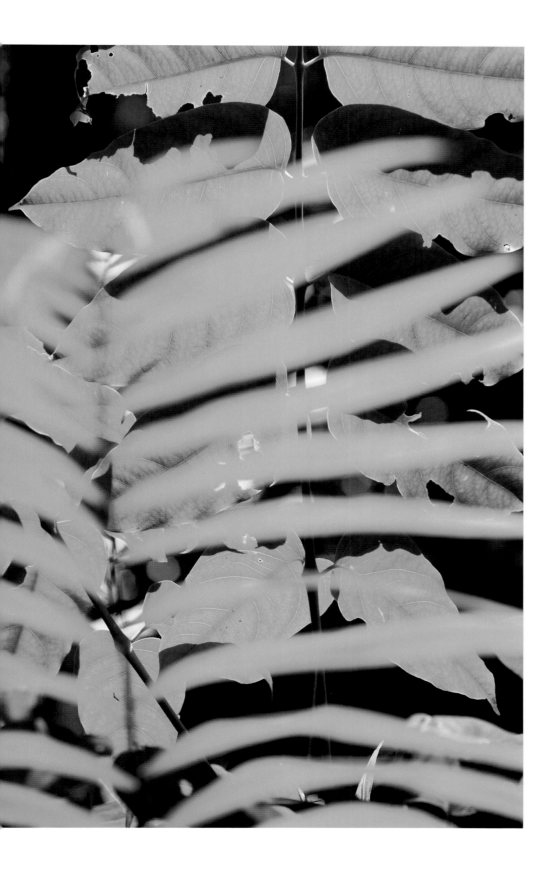

Adjacent page, top left:
Members of the public protesting at Grizedale Forest, Lake District, against the governments proposals to sell off Forestry Commission land.

Adjacent page, bottom:
An ancient Oak tree at Hartsop in the Lake District, Cumbria, UK. Trees provide an invaluable service to humanity by producing the oxygen that we breath and sequestrating much of the CO_2 that we emit. By chopping down the world's forests we significantly reduce their ability to soak up our emissions.

Adjacent page, top right:
Trees planted by the Australian Rainforest Foundation in the Daintree Rainforest. The foundation is committed to helping the rainforest to recover from the felling and destruction that has affected much of the forest cover. Its operations also help local businesses offset their carbon emissions.

Left:
A tropical palm tree in the Daintree Rainforest, Queensland, Australia. Rainforest habitat is a vital carbon sink and the lungs of the planet, but is being chopped down all across the planet. The Daintree is the oldest continuous forested rainforest on the planet.

Above:
The Curtain Fig Tree, a massive Green Fig Tree
(Ficus virens) on the Atherton Tablelands, Queensland,
Australia.

Above right:
Rainforest on steeply sloping ground on Fiji. Much of the
forest on lower slopes was chopped down decades ago.

Following page:
Looking down on deforested forest slopes from the air,
being replaced by farmland for subsistence agriculture
in Malawi. The country is suffering rapid deforestation,
to provide both land for farming and for making
charcoal, the main cooking fuel in Malawi.

Right:
Malawi is one of the poorest countries in the world, it has been heavily deforested. The deforestation has been to clear land for an expanding population to have access to land to grow subsistence crops and also to make charcoal, which is the main cooking fuel in Malawi. Here men carry timber illegally logged off the Zomba Plateau.

Adjacent page,top left:
A traditional dug out canoe being constructed from a chopped down tree in Malawi.

Adjacent page,bottom left:
Charcoal for sale on the roadside in Malawi. In this poor African country, charcoal is the main cooking fuel. Its production is driving high levels of deforestation. It takes 7 tonnes of wood to make 1 tonne of charcoal.

Adjacent page top right:
A Nepelese woman rests from carrying a heavy load of wood chopped down to be used as fuel for cooking, in the Annapurna Himalayas. Much of the native forest of the Himalayas has been heavily deforested by the local peoples, for whom, until recently it was their only source of power.

Adjacent page bottom right:
Tropical mountain forest in Bolivia near Coiroca, being deforested for agriculture. Bolivia has very high rates of deforestation, a disaster for biodiversity and for the climate.

Water resource

All humanity relies on a clean plentiful supply of water. Increasingly for many, it is becoming a scarce resource, and one that has been abused for decades. In the West, many of our rivers were highly polluted during the industrial revolution, only recently have we learned to clean up our act. Sadly in many areas of the world, this abuse of our river systems continues unabated. China is one of the biggest polluters, with many of China's waterways still being used as dumping grounds for toxic industrial waste. I witnessed water courses in China that were so impacted by drought, that the only liquid running in them was the toxic outpourings from factories. Vast swathes of Inner Mongolia, that used to be reasonably productive agricultural land, have been abandoned as the land has turned to desert, leaving whole villages empty. Many parts of China are so desperate for water that they have started a massive cloud seeding programme, where rockets loaded with silver iodide are shot into the sky in an attempt to try and make it rain. In California, one third of all children go to bed hungry, directly as a result of the drought that has resulted in thousands of agricultural workers being laid off. I visited families in Porterville, California who had been without running water in their homes for over 5 months and were reliant on water charities supplying bottled water for all their needs.

Right:
China's environmental protection standards are woefully inadequate. Many of their rivers as well as running dangerously low from over extraction and drought brought on by climate change are hideously polluted and litter strewn. In this riverbed in the industrial city of Hangang, the only running liquid is toxic waste from a nearby factory.

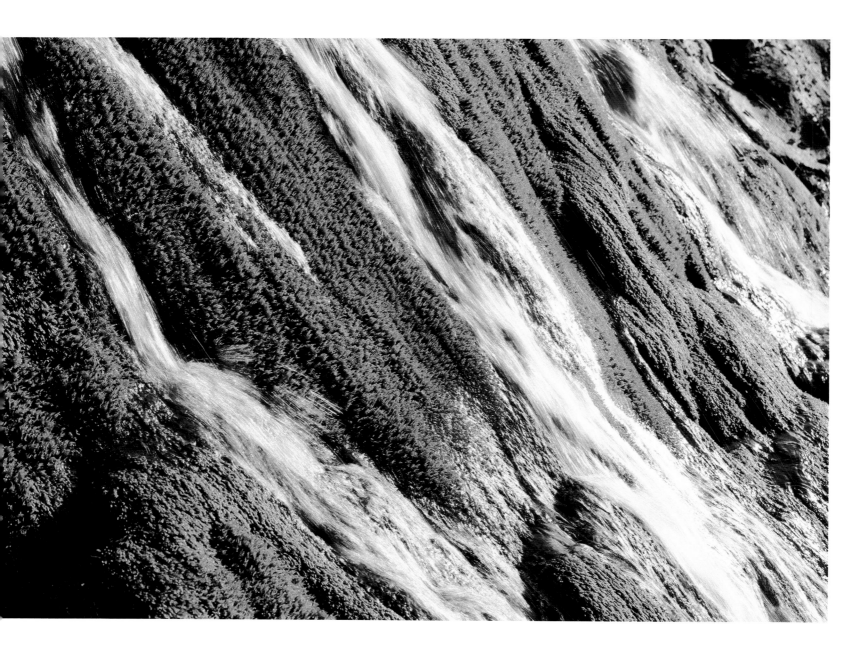

Above:
Pure water runs through a moss covered waterfall in Stanah Gill on the Helvellyn Range, Lake District UK. Climate change is increasingly making access to clean water a problem for many.

Above:
Reflections of warm evening light on clear water flowing over the weir at the outlet of Grasmere, Lake District, UK with foxgloves in the foreground.

Following page:
Looking down onto Loughrigg Tarn above valley mist, one of many clean, freshwater bodies in the Lake District National Park, UK.

Right:
Pollution floating against colours of a
fishing boat reflected in Oban harbour,
Scotland.

Adjacent page, top left:
Green algal sludge is all that remains
of an almost dried up lake at Tehachapi
Pass, California, USA.

Adjacent page, bottom left:
Contaminated water being emptied out of
Finland Docks in Hull, directly into the
Humber Estuary, Yorkshire, UK. The docks
are owned by Associated British Ports.
As they released the pollution, there was
an awful chemical stench in the air.

Adjacent page, top right:
The Bishnumati River running through
Kathmandu in Nepal. The river is full of
plastic garbage and raw sewage which is
emptied into the river. The local people see
the river as a rubbish collection service.
It symbolises all that is wrong in the way
that we treat the earths resources, that
ultimately we are utterly reliant on. This is a
composite image with the addition of a sign
that I photographed elsewhere in Nepal.

Adjacent page, bottom right:
A feather in contaminated mine effluent
from water draining out of Wheal Jane,
an abandoned tin mine near Redruth,
Cornwall, UK.

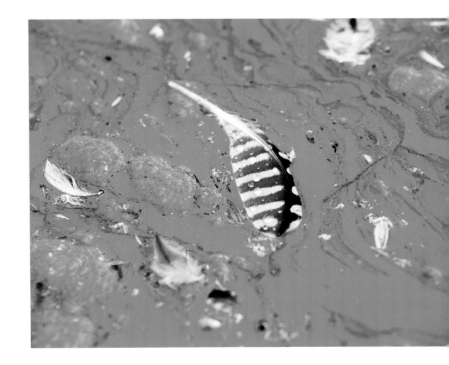

Adjacent page, top left:
Rare native White Clawed Crayfish killed by an illegal chemical spill on the River Mint near Kendal, Cumbria, UK.

Adjacent page, top right:
Irrigating crops in Skala Eresou on Lesvos, Greece, climate change models predict that the southern Mediterranean countries will become a lot hotter and drier with increased water security issues.

Adjacent page, bottom:
The California aqueduct bringing water from snowmelt in the Sierra Nevada mountains to farmland in the Central Valley, passing through drought scorched landscape. Following a four year long catastrophic drought, irrigation water is in short supply, causing $2 billion annually to be wiped off the agriculture sector.

Top left:
Two women on the Beach near Dahab on the Red Sea in Egypt walk past the return water pipe for a desalination plant. As many areas of the world become increasingly short of water they may have to turn to desalination for access to drinking water. Desalination consumes large amounts of energy.

Bottom left:
A man sits around a swimming pool at a holiday complex in Myrina on Lemnos, Greece.

Following page:
Sunrise over Lake Windermere in Ambleside, Lake District, UK, the largest lake in the National Park.

Green build
green transport

For most people in the developed world, their house represents the largest part of their carbon footprint. Heating and powering homes consumes vast quantities of energy, mostly powered by fossil fuel. We seem to have lost the ability to build houses, using local sustainable materials which are well insulated and efficient. Recently there has been a real growth in green construction, that is using renewable materials and technology to make buildings that are virtually carbon neutral to run. We have the technology to make housing more efficient, but we need to increase its uptake. It is far easier to build new efficient housing than it is to upgrade existing stock. In my own home, we have fitted additional loft insulation, double glazed windows and cavity wall insulation to try and make the building more thermally efficient. A wood burning stove provides a large percentage of our heat, reducing the need to use gas central heating. In addition we regularly cook on the wood burner, reducing the need to switch on a gas or an electric oven. On our roof we have fitted a solar thermal panel, which heats the water, again reducing our need to use gas. Solar PV panels on our roof produce around 3,000 kilowatt hours of electricity per year. Three quarters of our annual usage. That, in an area that is one of the wettest and cloudiest parts of the British Isles. In more sunny areas of the UK, you could easily generate all of your electricity requirements from a four Kilowatt PV system. At a time when the UK Government should be investing heavily in renewables they are completely rowing back and slashing subsidies for an industry that can provide thousands of green jobs. We need governments to provide far greater subsidies for renewable energy, to encourage its uptake. For every $1 spent by world governments on subsidies to renewable energy $6 is spent on subsidies to the fossil fuel industry.

Right:
A beautiful old barn with upper walls woven from split timber on a farm in Great Comberton, Vale of Evesham, Worcestershire, UK. Building using traditional local materials is usually the greenest method of construction.

Following page:
The ultra trendy, modern train station in Zaanstadt, which is designed to look like the traditional house style of the area, Netherlands. Its mainly wooden construction is very green.

Top right:
A greenhouse made from waste plastic
bottles and canes in the community
garden at Mount Pleasant Ecological
Park, Porthtowan, Cornwall, UK.

Bottom right:
A green build house being constructed
at 1,400 feet on Exmoor in Devon. The plot
is off grid and will be powered by a wind
turbine and solar panels. A bore hole will
provide the water. The building is timber
framed and will use hempcrete as the
wall insulation. The outbuildings are
straw bale construction.

Adjacent page, top:
Riverside One is a new concept in green
build in Middlesbrough, Teeside, UK.
It adheres to the ten principles of One
Planet living. It is an exceptional green
building, whose individual housing units
will have a low carbon footprint. The whole
block is heated by a biofuel boiler. During
construction it used recycled oil rig pipes
for piling, the concrete was mixed with
recycled aggregate, super insulated with
earth wool, it uses grey recycled water to
save water, locally sourced timber, the
electricity for the building is sourced from
renewable sources and the building
incorporates Swift bird boxes and bat boxes.
Residents are encouraged to car share and
use local organic vegetable box schemes.

Adjacent page, bottom left:
Navala village in the Fijian highlands, the
only village on the island composed entirely
of traditional Bure houses. A sustainable,
zero carbon form of contruction.

Adjacent page, bottom right:
An electric vehicle at a recharging station
in Berkeley Square, London, UK.

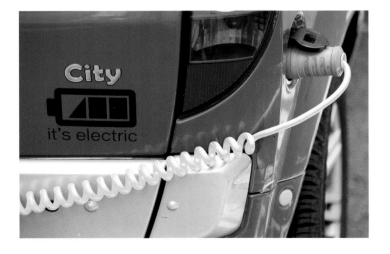

Adjacent page top left:
A cyclist on one of the new Cycle Superhighways, in this case the CS7 that goes from Southwark Bridge to Tooting in London. It makes cycling much safer and encourages more people to take their journey by bike, reducing congestion and the greenhouse gas emissions from other types of transport.

Adjacent page top right:
An Ampera electric car at a charging station for electric cars with a lady cycling her children to the shops in Ijburg, Amsterdam, Netherlands.

Adjacent page, bottom:
All of Delhi's buses run on Compressed Natural Gas (CNG), it is the worlds largest eco friendly bus fleet and has helped to improve Delhi's air quality, after they replace diesel buses, India.

Above left:
A workman at the construction of a new High Speed rail link between Antequera and Granada in Andalucia, Spain.

Left:
The Houses of Parliament and Big Ben with buses crossing Westminster Bridge, London, UK. Public transport has around half the carbon footprint of cars per mile travelled.

The affected

Climate change impacts most on the world's most vulnerable and marginalised people, sometimes out of sight out of mind, other times in the full glare of the world's media. Europe's refugee crisis is really a story of climate change. The Arab Spring started in Tunisia as a protest against the rising price of food. Prices that were rising directly as a result of shortages caused by drought. Drought in Syria, caused tens of thousands of folk to abandon the countryside and migrate to the cities. Protests by these displaced people are what lit the fuse for the ongoing war in Syria that has driven so many people out of their homes and caused them to flee and seek sanctuary in Europe.

Right:
A Syrian migrant family collapse in tears of relief
after safely landing on Lesvos, Greece.

Right:
The Boudanath Stupa, is one of the holiest Buddhist sites in Kathmandu, Nepal. Nepal has been hit hard by climate change, with rapidly changing weather systems impacting their basic agricultural systems.

Adjacent page,top left:
A mother and young baby, subsistence farmers in the Sunderbans, Ganges Delta, India. The area is very low lying and vulnerable to sea level rise. India has a rapidly expanding population. If humanity is serious about tackling climate change, we have to take a serious look at limiting population growth.

Adjacent page,bottom left:
An elderly man on Funafuti Atoll, Tuvalu.

Adjacent page top right:
Least responsible for climate change, but most impacted by it. An elderly Tuvaluan man using a traditional palm frond pillow, Funafuti, Tuvalu.

Adjacent page,bottom right:
Lola Everson, an Inuit village elder on Shishmaref. During her lifetime she has witnessed a massive change in weather patterns, most noticeably the lack of sea ice around their island home.

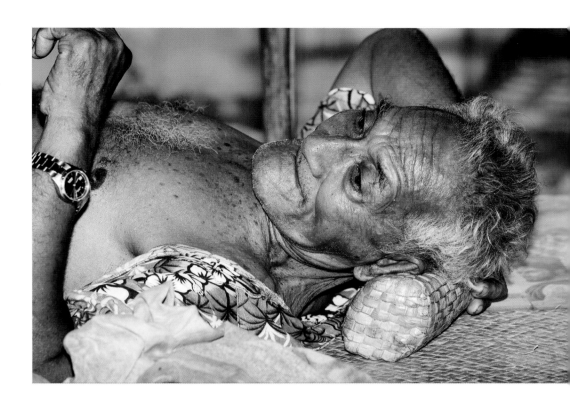

Adjacent page,top left:
An Aboriginal lady at the Tjapukai Aboriginal Park near Cairns, Queensland, Australia. Native Australians have been left with the most marginal of land and are very susceptible to climate change.

Adjacent page top right:
Robert Grandjamber a First Nation Canadian living in Fort Chipewyan, using a Moose call made from Birch bark to attract bull Moose whilst hunting.

Adjacent page,bottom left:
A Berber shepherd and his son outside a cave used as a night time shelter for goats and sheep in the Anti Atlas mountains of Morocco, North Africa. The drought in Morocco has left little vegetation for his flock to graze on.

Adjacent page,bottom right:
A Berber Arab in the Jebel Sirwa region of the Anti Atlas mountains of Morocco, North Africa. The area has been severely impacted by drought.

Left:
A Bedouin man cooking bread on an open fire in a camp in the Sinai Desert near Dahab in Egypt. Much of North Africa is getting consistently hotter and drier making it increasingly difficult to grow food crops.

Adjacent page, top left:
Syrian migrants fleeing the war and escaping to Europe, who have landed on the Greek island of Lesvos on the north coast at Efthalou, September 2015. Up to 4,000 migrants a day are landing on the island and overwhelming the authorities. They are trafficked by illegal Turkish people traffickers who charge up to $2,000 per person for a half hour ride in an overcrowded inflatable boat from the Turkish mainland to Lesvos. This mass migration of people is driven by climate change, as the Arab Spring which initiated the unrest in the Middle East started as a protest against high food prices. The prices of food rose dramatically as harvests collapsed as a result of climate change driven by drought in the region.

Adjacent page, top right:
Syrian migrants in Mytilini on Lesvos, Greece, with the Greek Army checking papers.

Adjacent page, bottom:
Syrian migrants in Mytilini on Lesvos, Greece.

Top left:
A father carries his daughter ashore. Syrian migrants landing on the north coast of Lesvos at Efthalou.

Bottom left:
An overcrowded Zodiak with Syrian migrants landing on the North coast of Lesvos at Efthalou.

Following page:
Syrian migrants landing on the north coast of Lesvos at Efthalou, surrounded by a sea of abandoned life jackets.

Protest

Too many of the world's politicians are in the pockets of the fossil fuel industry. Huge vested interest in fossil fuels means that they wield massive power, a power that they are using for narrow self interest. Most of the climate denying bodies are supported by fossil fuel money. The industry spends millions on lobbying politicians to promote inactivity and the status quo, as well as on promoting pseudo science. The industry is using the same tactics that were employed by the tobacco industry, when doctors first revealed that smoking caused lung cancer. We cannot rely on our politicians to take the action that is necessary. The stance taken by Canada (under Stephen Harper) and Australia (under Tony Abbott) should be singled out for particular criticism. Stephen Harper has formally withdrawn Canada from its commitments under the Kyoto Protocol to reduce its greenhouse gas emissions. Tony Abbott in Australia, is most famous for saying that climate science is "absolute crap". He has fought to scrap Australia's commitments to reduce greenhouse gases and is a staunch supporter of the coal industry.

Armed by the knowledge that we face a very uncomfortable future without a rapid decarbonisation, many people are choosing to take direct action. Fossil fuel companies have been directly targeted by protest groups, and there is a growing divestment campaign to get organisations to withdraw their support to the fossil fuel industry. The internet has allowed citizens to engage like never before. Many groups are campaigning and lobbying and citizens are coming together to demand action on climate change.

Right:
On Saturday 5th December 2009, the Stop Climate Chaos
Coalition organised the Wave. A demonstration against
climate change that attracted 50,000 people, who
surrounded parliament as part of the protest. London, UK.

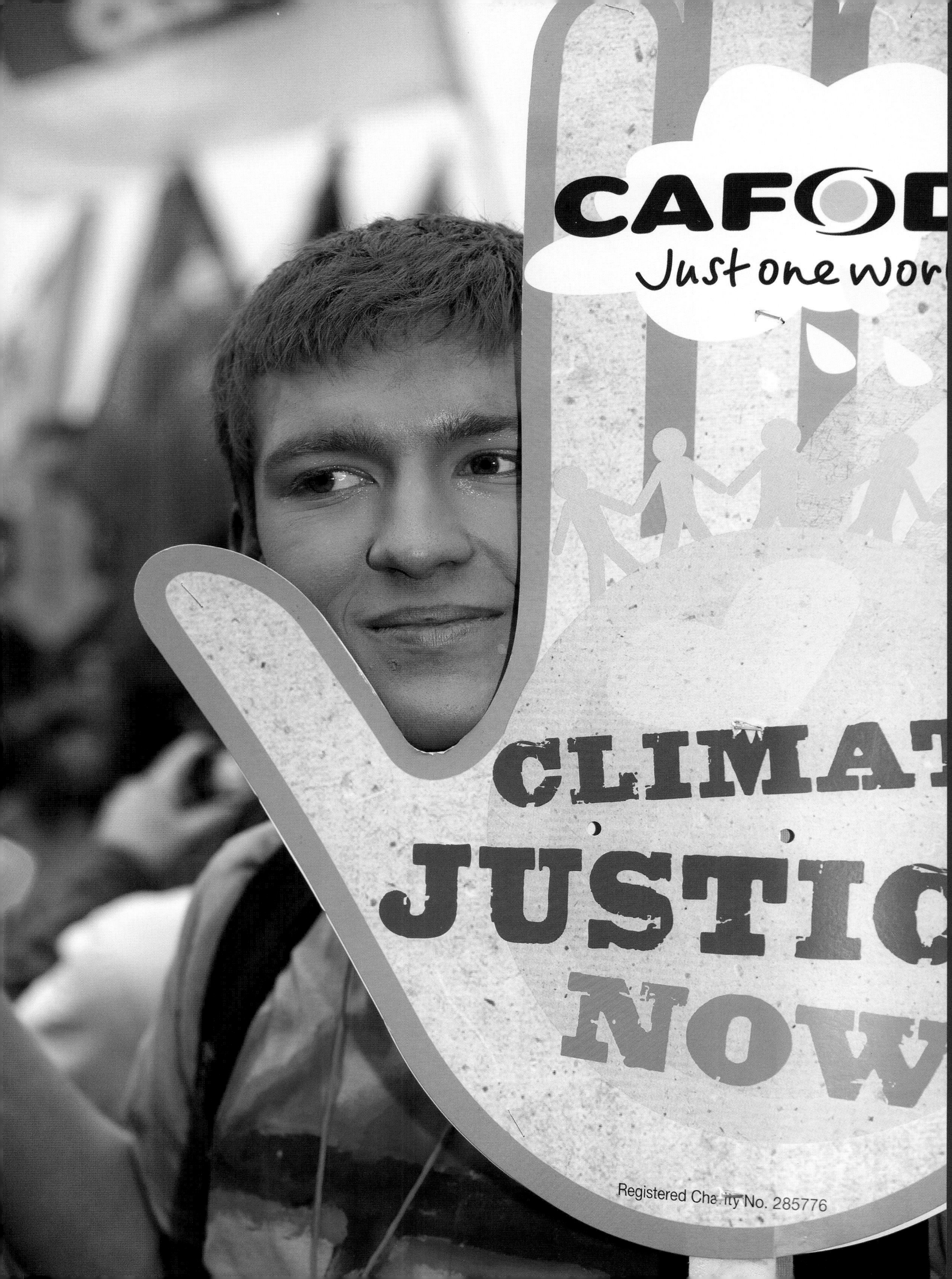
NOW

Right:
First Nation Canadians protest against the destruction and pollution by the Tar Sands industry, at the 4th annual Healing Walk north of Fort McMurray, Alberta. RCMP officers police the walk but are more interested in protecting vested interests of the wealthy oil companies than the lands of the indigenous people.

Bottom right:
First Nation Canadians protest against the destruction and pollution of the Tar Sands industry at the 4th annual Healing Walk north of Fort McMurray, Alberta, next to a tar sands plant.

Adjacent page, top left:
A protestor against fracking at a farm site at Little Plumpton near Blackpool, Lancashire, UK.

Adjacent page, top right:
The Climate Camp protest site that is opposing the plans to introduce a third runway at Heathrow, the world's largest airport.

Adjacent page, bottom:
Cuadrilla applied to frack for shale gas at several sites in Lancashire but was turned down by Lancashire County Council, after huge local opposition. Cuadrilla appealed the decision. Tuesday 9th February was the first day of the appeal hearing at which a huge anti fracking demonstration was organised. It is widely believed that whatever the appeals decision it will be overturned by the Conservative Government, who are hell bent on fracking for gas.

Adjacent page,top left:
Protestors at a climate change rally in London, December 2008.

Adjacent page top right:
Protestors at a climate change rally in Parliament Square, London in December 2008 with Big Ben behind.

Adjacent page,bottom:
Celebrities including the actor Peter Capaldi and the former BBC weatherman Michael Fish join The Wave climate change protest rally.

Left:
The Stop Climate Chaos Coalition, Wave protest beneath Big Ben. A demonstration against climate change that attracted 50,000 people.

Following page:
Climate change Protestors surrounding the Houses of Parliament, London, UK, as part of The Wave.

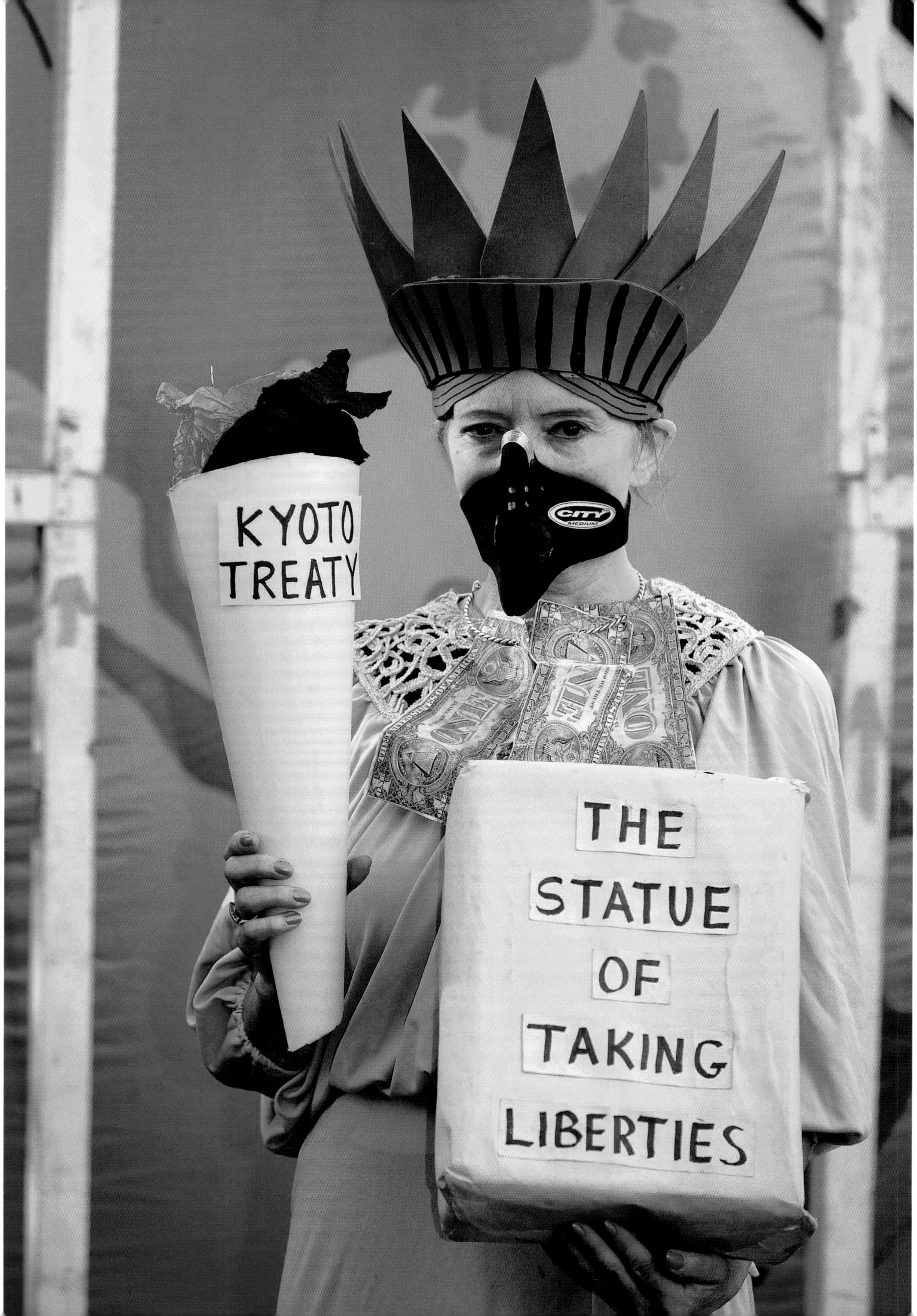
KYOTO
TREATY
CITY
THE
STATUE
OF
TAKING
LIBERTIES

Adjacent page:
A protestor dressed as the Statue of Liberty at the ICount, climate change rally outside the American Embassy in London, November 2006. A response to the USA's position on climate change under George Bush.

Top left:
A lady at an anti fracking protest in Blackpool, Lancashire, has the right idea. We need to move rapidly to a low carbon economy, and invest billions in renewables.

Bottom left:
The Artful, an Astute class hunter killer nuclear powered submarine is moved from BAE Systems in Barrow in Furness up to the Faslane submarine base in Scotland, UK. The submarines are armed with Spearfish torpedoes and Tomahawk Cruise missiles. There is an argument that nuclear power stations are the answer to generating low carbon electricity, though the reality is that current nuclear technology is the most expensive way of generating electricity ever invented.

Renewable energy

To stand any real chance of tackling climate change we need to move rapidly to a low carbon economy. We all have a responsibility to use less energy, and to make sure that the energy we do use comes from renewable sources. Recent studies have shown that the vast majority of fossil fuel reserves need to be kept in the ground. Going forward that leaves us with nuclear or renewable energy. Many countries are turning away from nuclear following the Fukushima nuclear accident. Leaving aside nuclear's toxic legacy, it is the most expensive form of electricity generation ever invented by man. This leaves us with only one option going forward, and that is massive investment in renewable energy. Many studies have shown that the world could be powered several times over by the potential that renewable technologies possess. They also have the added advantage that the pollution that blights many lives from the burning of coal and oil, will be eradicated, leaving cleaner air for all.

Right:
Andrea Wuenschel, one of 50 biologists working at The Ivanpah Solar Thermal Power Plant in California's Mojave Desert. Ivanpah is currently the largest solar thermal plant in the world. It generates 392 megawatts (MW) and deploys 173,500 heliostats that reflect the suns rays onto three solar towers. It covers 4,000 acres of desert. Andrea is looking out for birds that might be flying close to the solar towers.

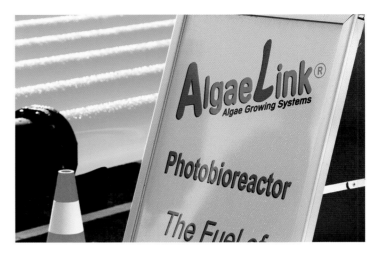

Adjacent page, top left:
The biofuel hopper at Farmgen's biodigester based at Dryholme Farm, near Silloth, Cumbria, UK.

Adjacent page, top right:
An Algae Link system that grows algae to make ethanol and biodiesel. Producing oil from algae in this way is much more efficient than from growing traditional plant oil crops like oil seed rape. It also has the benefit that it does not take up space that could be growing food crops.

Adjacent page, bottom:
The Farmgen anaerobic bio digestor at Dryholme Farm. The plant which cost £4.5 million, produces 1.2 Mw of electricity, enough to power 2,000 households. It uses around 25,000 tons of feedstock annually, mainly maize and grass, which is mixed with farm slurry and fed into the massive digestors where bacteria break it down. The resulting methane is what powers the electricity generator.

Top left:
The Steven's Croft biofuel power station in Lockerbie, Scotland. It is the largest wood fired biomass station in the UK with an output of 44MW, enough to power 70,000 homes.

Bottom left:
A woman in a remote subsistence farming village on an island in the Sunderbans, the Ganges Delta in Eastern India. She is cooking on a traditional clay oven, fuelled by biofuel (rice stalks), low carbon cooking.

Top left:
An old windmill at Cley Next the Sea, North Norfolk, UK. For centuries man has been harnessing the power of renewable energy, it is now time to ramp up the exploitation of this clean, green energy resource.

Bottom left:
Colourful wind turbines in polders, reclaimed land near Almere, Flevoland, Netherlands.

Adjacent page, top:
A modern take on the classic image of tulip fields and windmills. A wind farm and tulip fields near Almere, Flevoland, Netherlands.

Adjacent page, bottom left:
Old Chinese proverb

'When the winds of change blow, some people build walls whilst others build windmills'

Three wind turbines being constructed behind the Kirkstone Pass Inn in the Lake District, UK. Because of its remote location, the pub is not connected to the grid and currently spends £25,000 a year on a diesel generator. The wind turbines will vastly reduce the need for the generator and are the first wind turbines to get planning permission in the National Park.

Adjacent page, bottom right:
The Tehachapi Pass wind farm at sunrise.

Following page:
Part of the Tehachapi Pass wind farm, California, the first large scale wind farm area developed in the USA.

Above:

The Isle of Eigg off Scotland's west coast, shows the way forward to a renewable future. In 1997 the island was purchased from its feudal landlord by the Eigg Heritage Trust, a partnership between the islanders, the Highland Council and the Scottish Wildlife Trust. At that point the electricity was provided by each house having a noisy, polluting and expensive diesel generator, as the island is not connected to the grid. In 2008 the islanders decided to turn to a green solution. Eigg Electric was set up and developed a grid for the island with the energy produced by hydro schemes, wind turbines and solar panels. This is enough to power the homes of the 90 residents. Each is restricted to using 5Kw maximum at any one time. This avoids spikes in demand, which is the curse of all electric grids. The renewables power the island 98% of the time, with diesel generators automatically kicking in when needed. An array of batteries also stores excess production, giving the island a 24 hour backup if everything fails.

Above:
Jamie Ardagh, a crofter and Eigg Electric
employee amongst the array of backup
batteries that store sufficient to power
the island for 24 hours. One of the
greatest hurdles to overcome as we ramp
up production from renewables is
energy storage.

Adjacent page, top:
Dawn over Whitelee wind farm on Eaglesham Moor just south of Glasgow in Scotland. It is Europe's largest onshore wind farm with 215 turbines and an installed capacity of 539 MW.

Adjacent page, bottom left:
Workers at the Walney Offshore Windfarm, Barrow in Furness, Cumbria, UK, in front of wind turbine transition pieces. The wind farm was constructed and is owned by the Danish, Dong Energy company. It has the capacity to generate 367MW. Converting to a renewable future creates many green, sustainable jobs.

Adjacent page, bottom right:
Health and safety workers on a turbine at the Walney offshore wind farm.

Top left:
A massive crane lifts a 320 tonne transition piece onto the deck of a jack up barge, for the Walney offshore wind farm.

Bottom left:
The jack up barge, Goliath, loaded with transition pieces for the Walney Offshore wind farm project, is towed out into the Walney channel by a high powered tug.

Following page:
The jack up barge, Goliath lifting a 320 tonne transition piece into place on the Walney Offshore wind farm project. Construction work takes place 24 hours a day with two twelve hour shifts of workers. This shot was taken at 4.00 am.

Previous page:
The huge blades to be used at Walney offshore wind farm, the serrations help to control the air flow over the blade for greater efficiency and extra power.

Left:
A gantry linking the jack up barge, Kraken with a transition piece, of a wind turbine at Walney. The first of the tower pieces is being winched into place, with the workers waiting to screw it into place.

Top:
The Kraken, a jack up barge, that is constructing the wind turbines of the Walney offshore wind farm. It is using a specialist cradle to lift a turbine blade into place.

Above:
A health and safety inspector on a crew transfer vessel.

Right:
The Walney offshore wind farm under construction at dawn.

Bottom right:
Doug Parr, chief scientist for Greenpeace UK at Gunfleet Sands offshore wind farm. It consists of 48 turbines off Brightlingsea in Essex, UK, and has a capacity of 172 MW, enough to power 125,000 homes.

Adjacent page, top left:
A protest sign about a new wind turbine in Seaton near Workington, Cumbria, UK, with onshore wind turbines and the offshore Robin Rigg wind farm visible.

Adjacent page, bottom left:
Construction workers working on the foreshore of the Solway Firth near Workington, installing the power cable that will carry the electricity from Robin Rigg offshore wind farm.

Adjacent page, top right:
The Iznajar hydro electric power station near Antequera in Andalucia, Spain.

Adjacent page, bottom right:
The pipe being laid for the Scandale Beck hydro scheme, Lake District, UK.

Above:
Delivering hydro pipes for the new Scandale Beck hydro electric scheme, Ambleside, Lake District, UK.

Above:

Turbines in Murray 1 power station. Murray 1 is the second largest power station in Australia's Snowy Mountains hydro scheme. It has ten, 95 megawatt turbine generators. Each turbine can generate enough electricity to power 95,000 homes. The whole Snowy hydro scheme generates an average of 4,500 gigawatt hours per year and produces 11% of Australia's electricity. Sadly nearly all the rest of Australia's power generation is from coal fired power stations. The scheme also provides 2,360 gigalitres of irrigation water.

Left:
The outflow from the Karahnjukar
hydro scheme in Vatnajokull, Iceland.
It was created by damming the Jokuls
a Dal river. It is controversial as it
flooded a huge area of one of Europe's
last wilderness areas, that was home to
nesting Whooper Swans and Pink
Footed Geese. The project produces 40%
of Iceland's electricity from renewables.
The projects statistics are as follows:
power generation, 700MW, gross head,
600 metres, Max flow 144 M/sec,
Halslon Lake area 57KM squared,
storage volume 2.1 million metres, dam
height 198m (the tallest in Europe),
head race tunnels 73km. 100% of
Iceland's electricity is generated from
renewables, 70% from hydro and 30%
from geothermal.

Above:
The main high voltage electric cables
start their journey, from the underground
plant, to the outside pylons at Fljotsdalur
hydro power station part of Karahnjukar
a massive new hydro electricity project in
North East Iceland.

Adjacent page, top left:
Friends relax at the Blue Lagoon which uses hot water from a geothermal power station near Keflavik in Iceland.

Adjacent page, top right:
A geyser erupting at Geyser in Iceland, the place after which all the worlds geysers are named.

Adjacent page, bottom:
Hellisheidi geothermal power station in Hengill, Iceland is the worlds second largest geothermal power station. It will soon have a capacity of 300 MW of electricity generation. It also supplies hot water via a pipeline to Reykjavik for space heating for households and industry.

Top left:
Hveragerdi in South West Iceland sits on the Varma river and is a geothermal hot spot, with steam rising from fumeroles right in the middle of town. It has been used for nearly 100 years for growing vegetables in greenhouses using the geothermal heat. Here tomatoes are grown all year round using geothermal heat.

Bottom left:
A remote house lit by renewable electricity in Iceland, with the Northern Lights overhead.

Adjacent page, top left
A tidal energy turbine on the dockside in Kirkwall, Orkney, in Scotland. The Orkneys have developed a reputation as the marine energy capital of the world.

Adjacent page, top right
A hydrogen filling station on the outskirts of Reykavik, Iceland. The filling station is part of a project to help Iceland move away from imported oil and instead power its vehicles with hydrogen. Iceland is committed to moving to a hydrogen economy by 2050.

Adjacent page, bottom
Workman preparing to tow a Pelamis P2 wave energy generator on the dockside at Lyness on Hoy, Orkney Isles. The Orkney's have huge potential for wave and tidal energy generation and are world leaders in testing such devices. The Pelamis P2 is 180 metres long, weighs 1,300 tonnes and is rated at 750 Kw. It was the world's first commercial scale marine device to generate electricity to the grid, from offshore. The power is created from flexible joints that are linked to cylinders that pump liquid into high pressure accumulators to generate electricity.

Right:
A geothermal energy project by Newcastle University, funded by the Department of Energy and Climate Change. This project involves drilling 6,000 feet beneath Newcastle, on the site of the old Newcastle Brown Brewery. At this depth, the geothermally heated water is 80°C. The plan is for this renewable energy source to provide space heating for a shopping centre and University buildings.

Adjacent page, top:
Solar panels on the Cabanne D' Orny in the Swiss Alps, providing electricity for this off grid mountain hut at over 10,000 feet. In the background is the D' Orny glacier which is receding rapidly.

Adjacent page, bottom:
A family in front of their house in Almere with solar PV panels on the roof. It is the Netherlands youngest town having been reclaimed from the sea. This planned city is very green, with space heating provided from a nearby combined heat and power plant, and from Sun Island, a circle of solar thermal panels which provides hot water for the residents. Zoneiland contains 520 solar panels covering an area of approximately 7,000 square metres. Annually it provides 9,750 gigajoules of renewable, sustainable energy, equal to 10% of Almere city's total annual energy needs. The rest of the energy is provided by the local power plant in Almere.

Left:
Technicians fitting solar photo voltaic panels to my house roof in Ambleside, Cumbria. Although the Lake District is renowned for its wet, cloudy climate, with Ambleside receiving some 70 inches of rain annually, these panels generate three quarters of my electricity needs.

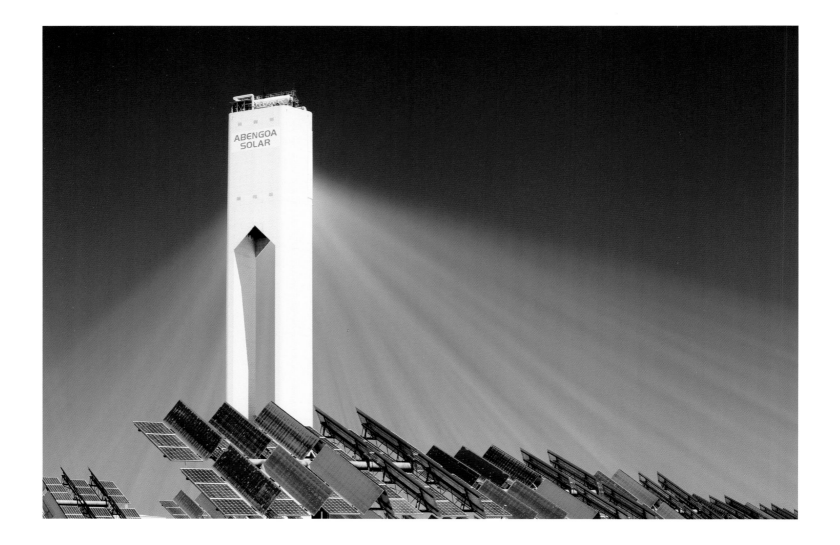

Adjacent page, top left:
A truck passes photo voltaic panels in part of the Solucar solar complex owned by Abengoa Energy, in Sanlucar La Mayor, Andalucia, Spain.

Adjacent page, top right:
The Andasol solar power station near Guadix in Andalucia, Spain, is the world's first solar thermal parabolic trough power station. It was opened in 2009 and produces around 180 gigawatt hours per year, providing enough energy for around 200,000 people. It has a thermal storage system where molten salt stores the heat energy that can continue to turn the turbines for up to 7 hours, after sunset, or if the sun goes in. A wind farm in the background is also producing carbon neutral renewable energy.

Adjacent page, bottom:
The PS20 solar thermal tower. It is part of the Solucar solar complex owned by Abengoa Energy, in Sanlucar La Mayor, Andalucia, Spain. The site has solar tower, parabolic trough and photovoltaic solar technology on the complex.

Above left:
Heliostats, large reflective mirrors directing sunlight to the PS20 solar thermal tower.

Bottom left:
Tracking photovoltaic solar panels at sunset at the Solucar solar plant in Sanlucar La Mayor.

Left:
A photo voltaic solar power station
near Caravaca, Andalucia, Spain, with
wild flowers.

Above:
Part of the Solucar solar complex owned
by Abengoa Energy, in Sanlucar La Mayor,
Andalucia, Spain. The site has solar tower,
parabolic trough and photovoltaic solar
technology.

Above:
Workers washing the heliostats to maximise
reflective power at the Ivanpah Solar Thermal
Power Plant, Mojave Desert, California, USA.

Above:
Two of the three solar towers and heliostats
at Ivanpah Solar Thermal Power Plant, Mojave
Desert, California, USA.

Above:

The new floating solar farm being grid connected on Godley Reservoir in Hyde, Manchester, UK. The scheme is a 3 MW system, comprising of 10,000 photo voltaic panels. It will cut United Utilities electricity bill at the water treatment plant on site, by around £7,000 a month. It is the largest floating solar farm in Europe and the second largest in the world. It will provide around 33% of the water treatment plants energy needs.

Above:
The Chinese are investing heavily in renewable energy
projects. Zhang Xinru an ethnic South Korean emigre living
near Suihua city in northern China poses in front of her
new house built by the local Communist Party, with solar
thermal panels on the roof.

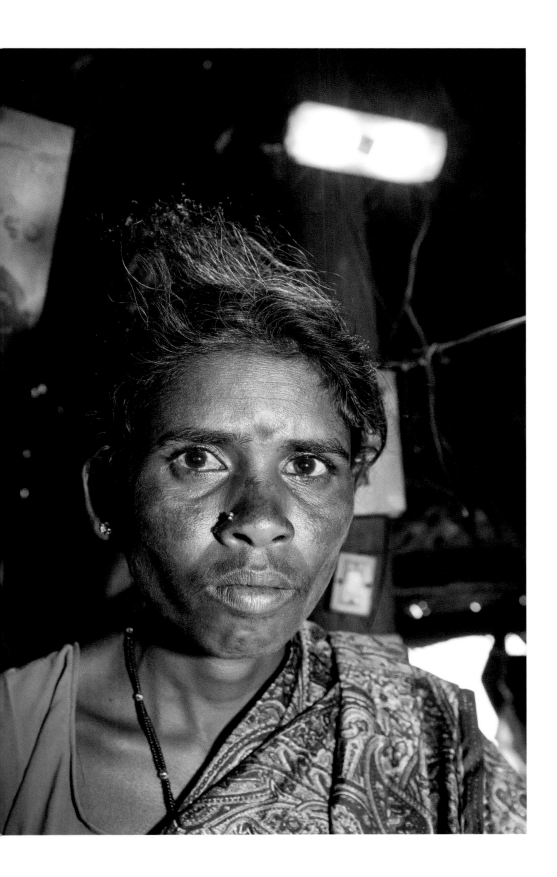

Adjacent page, top left:
A WWF project to supply electricity to a remote island in the Sundarbans, a low lying area of the Ganges Delta in Eastern India, that is very vulnerable to sea level rise. Prior to this project the subsistence farmers had no access to electricity. The project involves charging large batteries from solar panels. Each villager collects a battery to run household lighting and returns to the recharging station once a week to recharge their battery.

Adjacent page, top right:
Illumination being provided by a kerosene lamp in a house in the Sundarbans, India. Over 1 million woman and children die each year from the affects of inhaling kerosene fumes.

Adjacent page, bottom:
An untouchable family outside their hut, which is now illuminated by an electric light, powered by an A4 sized solar panel, that charges a battery. The project was sponsored by the Mysore Rotary club.

Left:
An untouchable woman in her hut, illuminated by an electric light, powered by an A4 sized solar panel, that charges a battery, and enables her to have light. Before the installation of the solar panels, the houses would be lit by kerosene lamps.

Far left, top:
Women carrying heavy twenty Kg batteries from a WWF run solar charging station in the Sundarbans, India.

Far left, bottom:
The Kamal factory in Bangalore, Karnataka, India, that manufactures solar thermal panels for heating water.

Left:
The Muni Seva Ashram in Goraj, near Vadodara, India, is a tranquil haven of humanitarian care. The Ashram is hugely sustainable, next year it will be completely carbon neutral. Its first solar panels were installed in 1984, long before climate change was on anyone's agenda. Their energy is provided from solar panels and wood grown on the estate. Waste food and animal manure is turned into biogas to run the estate's cars and also used for cooking. Solar cookers are also used, and the air conditioning for the hospital is solar. 70% of the food used is grown on the estate. They provide an orphanage, schools for all ages, vocational training, care for the elderly, a specialist cancer hospital with state of the art machinery and even have a solar crematorium. This shot shows solar panels that focus the suns rays on heat exchangers to heat oil, which is then sent down to the kitchens below to heat the cookers.

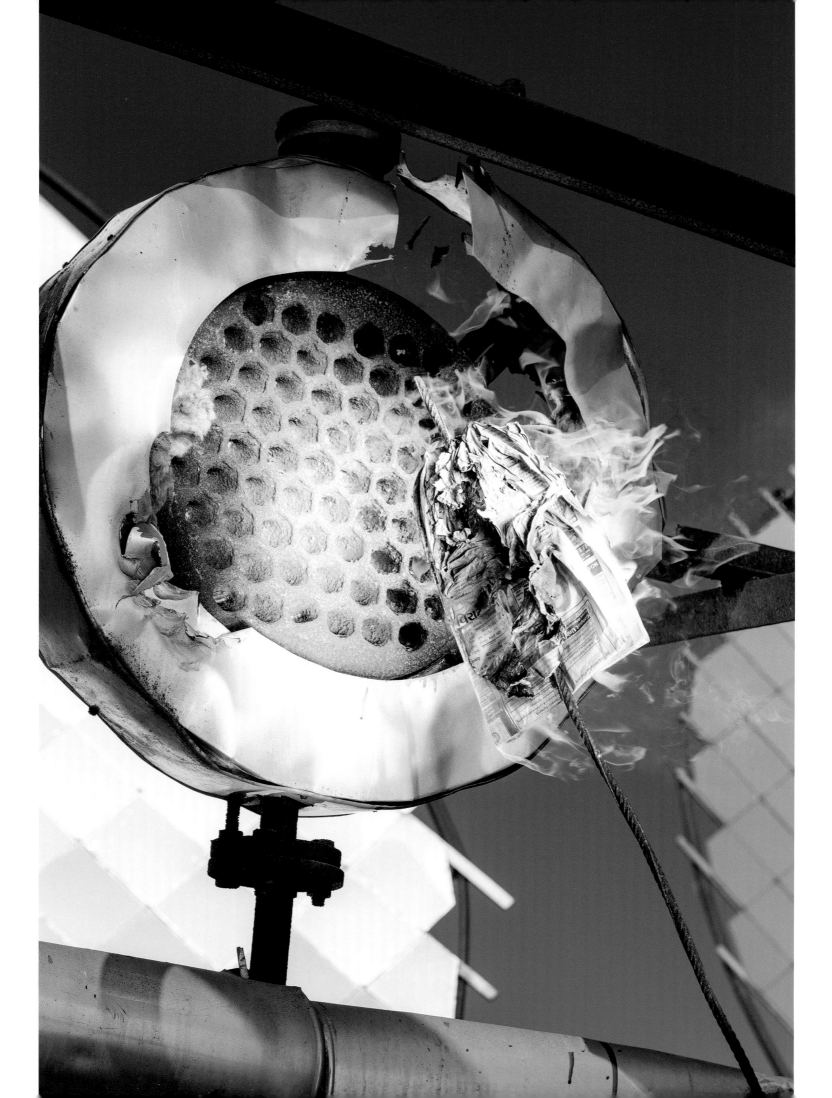

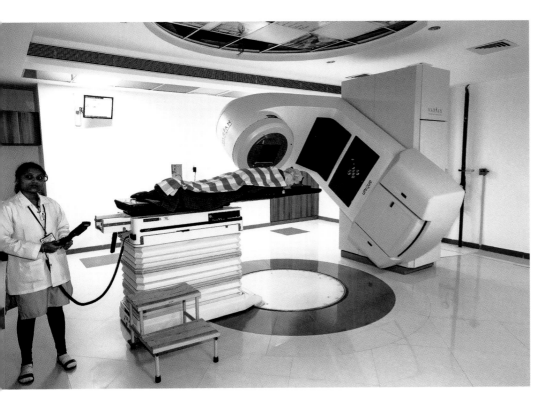

Adjacent page:
A newspaper is held in front of the rays from solar concentrating mirrors that instantly sets on fire in the 300°C heat. Muni Seva Ashram, Goraj, India.

Top left:
Deepak Gadhia by the world's first solar crematorium. It can burn a body completely in two hours, and can deal with four bodies a day. It has been designed to be strictly in accordance with the Hindu faith. The use of solar eliminates the need to cut down forest for wood to build a funeral pyre. Deepak Gadhia was a successful Indian business man, but following the death of his wife, decided to dedicate the rest of his life to promoting renewable energy and helping the Muni Seva Ashram.

Bottom left:
A cancer patient receives treatment from a Varian nuclear proton therapy machine in the specialist cancer hospital at the Muni Seva Ashram in Goraj, India. The Ashram is almost entirely run on renewable energy.

Right:
A women constructing a solar cooker at the Barefoot College in Tilonia, Rajasthan, India. The Barefoot College is a worldwide charity, founded by Bunker Roy. Its aims are: education, drinking water, electrification through solar power, skill development, health, women empowerment and the upliftment of rural people. The use of the cookers vastly reduces the amount of fire wood women have to go out and collect from the forest.

Top:
A women welding joints during the construction of a solar cooker at the Barefoot College.

Bottom:
Indonesian women in front of a solar cooker that they have learnt to build at the Barefoot College.

Far left:
Hotitode, a woman from Togo on a solar workshop, learning how to make solar lanterns at the Barefoot College. Many of the women are illiterate or semi literate. They are trained from countries all over the world, so that they can take their skills back and cascade the learning.

Left:
A solar cooker for baking bread at Annapurna Base Camp, Himalayas, Nepal.

Following pages:
Climate change photographer, Ashley Cooper stopped by police. Photographing the impacts of climate change seems to arouse the suspicions of the police, who stop me on a regular basis. When Police chiefs complain about their numbers being cut which will impact their ability to tackle crime, I remember the following. In 2007, the Metropolitan Police managed to find a vehicle and four police officers to tail me around London for seven hours, during which time I was stopped and searched twice for no reason. My crime at the time, documenting the climate camp protest against a third runway at Heathrow.
You would have thought that in the whole of London there may have been an actual crime needing investigating.

Policing climate change

Climate change is the greatest threat that humanity has ever faced. The job of the police is to protect the public. You might think therefore that the police might be interested in climate change. My experience over the last twelve years is that the police are interested in protecting big business, vested interest and the status quo. When it comes to climate change, anyone who the police deem to be an activist, protestor, or simply someone interested in the facts, are strangely viewed as enemies of the state. I have lost count over the years, how many times I have been stopped by the police and hassled by security guards. When pointing a camera at anything industrial, the police's view is at best you are up to no good, or at worst you are some kind of terrorist. They don't seem to be able to understand you might merely be a photographer going about your law abiding profession. Outside of the capital I have found most police to be friendly and in some cases even very helpful. The Metropolitan Police are a completely different story. Whilst documenting the climate camp that was protesting against a proposed third runway at Heathrow, I saw at first hand their intimidating tactics. On my first day I was stopped and searched twice. On the second day I awoke from my accommodation to find a large police four-wheel drive vehicle and four officers, inspecting my car. They searched my car for a third time. I set off back towards the climate camp and soon realised they were tailing me. Four Metropolitan Police officers then spent the next five hours following me. On occasions running red lights to catch up with me when I was a little ahead. When I stopped, they stopped. The second time I stopped, they thought it would be fun to body search me. In my work as a mountain rescue volunteer, I work on behalf of Cumbria Police. It would have taken the Met one phone call to verify who I was and what I do. Instead they spent over six hours trailing me around London. I later found out that they had committed vast resources to the climate camp, expecting trouble. As usual these protests are completely peaceful, so the police had nothing to do, other than photograph and video as many of the protestors as they could.

In 2008 a press release put out by the Metropolitan Police following the climate change protests at Kingsnorth coal fired power station, said that seventy of their officers had been injured whilst policing the protest. One would not unreasonably make the assumption from this statement that the officers were injured when tackling violent protestors. This indeed was the picture that

the Met. wanted to paint of the protestors. The Liberal Democrats submitted a freedom of information request to the Met. regarding the injuries the officers sustained. The list would have been laughable, if it wasn't such a serious attempt to smear the climate change protest movement. The list of injuries read, 'stung by wasp, tripped up getting out of car, heat stroke, etc'. Not one injury was caused by any of the climate camp protestors.

Crossroads

We are at a crucial crossroads in human history. We can carry on a 'business as usual' approach, and condemn ourselves to a very uncertain and dangerous future, or we can choose a clean, fairer future for all.

My mission to document the impacts of climate change on every continent has been a huge privilege. I have met many people along the way, that share my own love of life and love of all life on our precious planet. Equally I have met many people whose lives have already been ripped apart by the impacts of climate change. I have met people who have dedicated their lives to helping to provide their fellow citizens with electricity from renewable sources. I have seen much that is deeply depressing. The corruption and scale of destruction of the Canadian tar sands is truly shocking and horrifying to witness. Going forward, we have to remain optimistic, and we have to choose a clean future.

Right:
Bankers and economists of the world take note and wake up
before it is too late.

Following page:
We are at a crossroads and need to face the future, do we
carry on with our addiction to fossil fuels, committing
ourselves to devastating climate change. Or do we transition
rapidly to a renewable future. An oil terminal in Amsterdam,
Netherlands, with wind turbines generating renewable energy.

Left:
We are at a tipping point and have a choice to make, do we continue with business as usual and destabilise the climate or choose a low carbon future. Nicholas Coolridge and his partner Eve perform balance moves in Yosemite National Park, California.

Above:
This protest banner at a climate change rally in London, sums it all up.

Above:
A message to the earth spelt out with cherry blossom. We only have the one, we need to cherish it and treat it with the respect that our life support system deserves.

Above:

On Thursday 28th January 2016 Greenpeace UK handed in a petition to Downing Street protesting about the recent catastrophic flooding. As part of the day, an art installation of Wellington Boots were placed outside the Houses of Parliament. On each pair of boots a message was attached from someone who had been affected by the floods. It seemed fitting that after thirteen years travelling the planet to document climate change that my journey should end here. Helping to get the climate change message across to government.

397

Biography

Ashley gained a BSc Hons in Physical Geography from the University of Wales, Aberystwyth in 1983. Entering the marketplace in the era of Maggie's Millions, Ashley decided to return to his holiday job as a bin man for the Ribble Valley Borough Council, alongside evening bar work to earn enough money to go travelling. The low point of this career move was on Mondays, when he was placed on the affectionately named 'shit tanker'. This lorry toured the properties that were not attached to mains sewerage and didn't have a septic tank. A metal bucket with a wooden plank over the top was to be found in the toilet shed in back yards. These metal buckets had to be emptied once a week.

Ashley first decided to travel to Malawi to meet with a school friend who was working as a volunteer teacher there. In those days you could not fly direct to Malawi, but had to go via Lusaka in Zambia. During the stop over he decided to explore the shanty town outskirts of the city, with camera and binoculars around his neck. Unbeknown to him, the headquarters of the ANC in exile were based in Lusaka, and the week before his visit the South African security services had sent a hit squad to blow it up. The Zambians were understandably paranoid about South African spies. He was approached by a group of teenagers who accused him of being a South African spy. Ashley decided the best course of action was to leg it. A keen runner, he outran the mob, thinking he had escaped, only moments later to be arrested by the Zambian police on suspicion of being a South African spy. For an ardent Mandela fan this was the ultimate insult. Thankfully he was released to carry on his journey to Malawi, after some worrying hours thinking of Midnight Express.

It was whilst in Malawi that Ashley saw at first hand the work of LEPRA, the British Leprosy Relief Association. He returned to the UK, determined to help. The idea of a continuous expedition to climb every 3,000 foot mountain in Great Britain and Ireland was hatched. Six months of planning later Ashley set off on the 10th May 1986. Little did he know that this was to be the coldest and wettest spring/summer on record in Scotland, where most of the 3,000 footers are to be found. 111 days later, Ashley became the first person to climb every 3,000 foot peak in Great Britain and Eire in one continuous expedition. The walk was over 1,450 miles with over 500,000 feet of ascent. It rained and /or snowed on 93 of the 111 days, with few views from the tops. Ashley came close to being killed on three occasions. The first when 120 mph winds bowled him across an ice plateau and threatened to tear him off the mountain and over a 600 foot cliff, the second when he was avalanched in the

Cairngorms, and the third when he realised he was stood on the cornice overhanging the 2,000 foot northern cliffs of Ben Nevis, in a total white out. The feat has not been repeated to this day, but more importantly raised £14,000 for LEPRA. Ashley returned to Malawi in 1987 to see at first hand, how the money he had raised was being spent. One of the proudest moments of his life was meeting the many leprosy sufferers being treated by LEPRA. The funds raised paid for over 1,000 people to be treated. Returning home Ashley moved to the Lake District to take up a job with Europa Sport, who had sponsored all his mountaineering equipment for the walk.

In 1990 Ashley was employed by the NSPCC, as the Appeals Manager for Cumbria. When he started, the child protection charity had one service unit based in Carlisle. Working closely with volunteers over the next twenty years, Ashley raised over £4 Million for services to children in Cumbria, and launched separate appeals to raise the money to open up an additional three child protection teams.

In 2010 Ashley won the climate change category of the Worldwide Environmental Photographer of the Year Competition. His work is published widely in newspapers, books, magazines and on TV around the world. In 2013, Ashley documented what was probably the first known incident of a Polar Bear starving to death directly as a result of climate change. The photograph was run as the lead, front page story in the Guardian newspaper.

For the last thirteen years Ashley has been travelling the world, documenting the impacts of climate change, the last seven of which have been full time. His travels have taken him to over thirty countries and every continent on the planet. His passion for the subject is fuelled by the knowledge that climate change poses the greatest threat that humanity has ever faced.

Ashley has been a team member of the Langdale/Ambleside Mountain Rescue Team for the last twenty three years. The team is one of the busiest in the UK, averaging over 100 rescues a year. He has had spells as both Team Secretary and Chairman.

Ashley lives in Ambleside with his wife Jill and Border Collie, Tag.

IMAGES FROM A WARMING PLANET

Acknowledgements

A project of this magnitude would not have been possible without the help and support of many people...

Jill, who allowed me the freedom to pursue my dreams.

Jonathon Porritt for generously writing the foreword and his support of this project.

John Beatty, whose stunning audio visual displays of the natural world first inspired me to pick up a camera, and whose support and encouragement of my early work was invaluable.

David Williams, at Impact International, who generously underwrote the entire cost of the book design.

Martin Gallagher at Zinco, for his amazing design work on the book.

Richard Little for help, advice and guidance.

Kate Rawles for invaluable help and advice and guidance.

Tony West for kindly shooting my Kickstarter video.

Sue Grimwood at Steppes Travel for help with organising photo shoots to Svalbard and Antarctica.

Gates Travel, who helped with travel plans on many of my photo shoots.

Aaron Lawton of One Ocean Expeditions in helping with the Svalbard and Antarctica photo shoots.

To the following scientists for allowing me access to their work: Jeff Warburton, Ian Bartholomew, Robert Simpson, Anthony Long, Sarah Woodroffe,

Aarti Khosla of WWF India, for organising the India Photo Shoot.

Paul Sunters of WWF International.

Dong Energy, for access to the Walney offshore wind farm.

NRG, for access to Ivanpah solar plant.

European Marine Energy Centre, Orkney, for access to wave and tidal energy projects.

Newcastle University for access to their geothermal energy project.

Landsvirkjun for access to hydro and geothermal power stations in Iceland.

The Barefoot College for access to their amazing educational projects to teach women how to make solar lanterns and solar cookers.

Gujarat Solar Park for access to their solar power station.

Muni Seva Ashram, for access to their inspiring charity projects, all powered by renewable energy.

Abengoa Energy for access to the Solucar Solar complex.

Farmgen for access to their biogas projects.

Jamie Ardagh of Eigg Electric, for access to their renewable energy projects.

The Inuit community of Shishmaref for welcoming me and giving me access to their vanishing world.

The residents of Tuvalu, for an equally warm welcome whilst documenting sea level rise.

Alan McBride for ideas and proof reading the image captions.

John Broughton and Mike Withers, for support, company and friendship on some of my photo shoots.

Eric Hilaire of the Guardian Newspaper for support of my work over many years.

Mark Van Ommen for help with Amsterdam's floating houses.

Dr John O'Conner for taking the time to share his amazing experience of intimidation at the hands of the Canadian government.

Clara Mercer, a First Nation resident of the tar sands region, for allowing me to share her cancer story.

The residents of Fort Chipewyan for sharing their downstream tar sands experiences with me.

United Nations World Food Programme for allowing me on their helicopter aid flight to Makhanga, Malawi.

Medecins Sans Frontieres for allowing me to document their work in helping flood refugees.

Alex Floyd at Concern Universal for help in accessing the Malawi flood refugee camps.

The residents of Porterville who shared their drought experiences with me.

The Iceland tourist board for supporting my photo shoot to Iceland.

The Syrian migrants who graciously allowed me to document their plight.

The Kamal factory in Bangalore for allowing me access to document their solar thermal factory.

400

The project has also received generous
donations from the following people...

June Young
Mike Bertioli
Andy and Caroline Caple
Colleen Carter
Helen Verity
Jill Halton
Paul Gilding
Jenny and Chris Ellins
Trishia Gough
Dave Barrington
Steve Fairburn
Daphne Watson
Bill and Sheila Fisher
Duarte Silveira
Ranjini Renvoize
Isabel Gordon
Derek Cook
John Mulholland
Jonathan Ward
Edwina Saunders
Lin Macintosh
Dave Higgs
Kate and Jim Moorey
Gaynor Thomasson
Nigel and Linda Kingdon
Keith Snell
Martin Gallagher
Michael Dawson
Julia and Martin Eddy
Heather and Geoff Davenport
Stephanie Barton
John Barwise
Hans Joergen Rasmusson
Andrew Nelson
Gill Kelly
Pete Martin
David and Debbie Churcher
Keith and Angela Churcher
Mark Baines
Jonathon Porritt
Lisa and Gavin Yule

Martin and Carol Scrowston
Helen Croxford
Ian and Susan Cunliffe
Ken and Wendy Capps
Ian Roderick
Janet Maxwell
Julia Laverack
Terry Sloan
John Fleetwood
Peta Rowan
Frank and Val McKee
Mira Barhillel
Rob and Karen Hill
Alastair Harrison
Jon Sparks
Alison Peak
Val and Andrew Sunderland
Peter and George Harvey
Mike Withers
John and Anita Payne
Pam Williamson
Richard Jarvis
John Broughton
Barbara Milne Redhead
Michelle Spaul
David Penn
Christina Gomaa
Joe Human
Michael Evans
Rachel Pain
Joyce Dalton
Science Photo Library
Christine Macfarlane
Tim and Beth Ripper
Michel Schinz
Andy Carling
Jeff Warburton
Les Telford
Jane and Cedric Beenstock
Eileen and Peter Davenport
Patricia Howell
Bill and Margery Grudgings
Tom Walmsley
Janet and Rob Wittington

Rod Amy
Tony Richards
Zoe Cooper
Stephanie and Andrew Burgess
Una and Les Gordon
Andrew Smith
Kevin Thackray
Steven Chapman
Mike McVey
Tony and Beverley Cooper
Jill Cooper
Kerry Holden
Ann Fielding
Ray and Gill Lane
Kati Brown
Keith Jones
David Chew
Tom Davenport
Katherine Davenport
Penny Dyer
Andrew Woodhead
David Crookhall
Erica Pulley
Alec and Claire McCarthy
Chris Turner

Image index

Front endpapers:
Death Valley,
California, USA.

Half title page:
Iceberg, Antarctic
Peninsular.

Title page:
Storm clouds,
Cumbria, UK.

Page 3:
The Langdale Pikes,
Lake District, UK.

Page 7:
Energy from
the sun.

Page 8-9:
Broch of Gurness,
Orkney, UK.

Page 10-11:
Setting sun,
Cumbria, UK.

Page 13:
M1 Motorway, UK.

Page 14:
Queens Mill,
Burnley, UK.

Page 16-17:
Seal Sands,
Teeside, UK.

Page 18:
Oil tankers Persian
Gulf, near Dubai.

Page 19:
RAF Red Arrows,
Windermere, UK.

Page 20-21:
Ineos Oil Refinery.
Grangemouth,UK.

Page 22:
Tata Steel, Ijmuiden,
Netherlands.

Page 23:
Seal Sands,
Teeside, UK.

Page 24-25:
Ineos Oil Refinery.
Grangemouth,UK.

Page 26-27:
Port Waratah,
Australia.

Page 28-29:
Drift Coal Mine,
NSW, Australia.

Page 30:
Dongsheng, Inner
Mongolia, China.

Page 31:
Heihe, Chinese
Russian Border.

Page 32:
Inner Mongolia,
China.

Page 33:
Suihua, Heilongjiang
Province, China.

Page 34:
Ratcliffe on Soar,
Nottingham, UK.

Page 35:
Fracking near
Southport, UK.

Page 36:
Teesmouth,
Harbour, UK.

Page 37:
Barrow in Furness,
Cumbria, UK.

Page 38:
Oildale, California,
USA.

Page 39:
Nome, Alaska, USA.

Page 40:
Bakersfield,
California, USA.

Page 41:
Taft, California, USA.

Page 42:
Daqing Oil Field
Northern China.

Page 43:
Island of Flotta,
The Orkney's, UK.

Page 44-45:
Daqing Oil Field
Northern China.

Page 46-47:
Assynt, Scotland.

Page 48:
Euston Road,
London, UK.

Page 49:
M60 Motorway,
Manchester, UK.

Page 50-51:
Dubai, United
Arab Emirates.

Page 52
Manchester
Airport, UK.

Page 53:
Jet engine.

Page 54:
River Thames,
London, UK.

Page 55:
Addiction to energy.

Page 55:
Melbourne,
Australia.

Page 56:
Ambleside, Lake
District, UK.

Page 57:
Las Vegas, USA.

Page 58:
The Illuminations,
Blackpool, UK.

Page 59:
Mountain Rescue,
Lake District, UK.

Page 61:
Dragonfly stuck in
tar sand, Canada.

Page 62:
Fort McMurray,
Canada.

Page 64:
North of Fort
McMurray, Canada.

Page 65:
Tailbacks near Fort
McMurray, Canada.

Page 65:
Athabasca, Alberta,
Canada.

Page 66:
Fort McMurray,
Alberta, Canada.

Page 67:
Fort McMurray,
Alberta, Canada.

Page 68:
Fort McMurray,
Alberta, Canada.

Page 68:
The Syncrude Mine,
Alberta, Canada.

Page 69:
The Syncrude Mine,
Alberta, Canada.

Page 69:
The Syncrude Mine,
Alberta, Canada.

Page 69:
A hand full of
raw tar sand.

Page 70:
Fort McMurray,
Alberta, Canada.

Page 71:
The Syncrude Mine,
Alberta, Canada.

Page 72-73:
Fort McMurray,
Alberta, Canada.

Page 74:
Fort McMurray,
Alberta, Canada.

Page 75:
Fort McMurray,
Alberta, Canada.

Page 75:
Fort McMurray,
Alberta, Canada.

Page 76:
Fort Mackay,
Alberta, Canada.

Page 76:
Fort Mackay,
Alberta, Canada.

Page 77:
Fort Chipewyan,
Alberta, Canada.

Page 77:
Lake Athabasca,
Alberta, Canada.

Page 79:
Refugee Camp,
Phalombe, Malawi.

Page 80:
A44, west of
Worcester, UK.

Page 80:
Whitehaven Harbour
Cumbria, UK.

Page 81:
Blackpool, UK.

Page 81:
Aberystwyth, Wales.

Page 81:
Whitehaven,
Cumbria, UK.

Page 82:
Mull Head on
Deerness, UK.

Page 83:
Washed ashore off
Blackpool, UK.

Page 84:
Walney Island,
Cumbria, UK.

Page 84:
Mallaig, Scotland,
UK.

Page 85:
Blackpool, UK.

Page 86:
Cumbria, UK.

Page 86:
Rydal, Lake
District, UK.

Page 87:
Shap, Cumbria, UK.

Page 87:
Langdale Valley
Lake District, UK.

Page 88:
Above Grasmere,
Lake District, UK.

Page 88:
Kirkstone Pass,
Lake District, UK.

Page 89:
Kentmere, Lake
District, UK.

Page 89:
Helvellyn Range,
Lake District, UK.

Page 90-91:
Red Screes Tarn,
Lake District, UK.

Page 92:
Derwentwater,
Lake District, UK.

Page 93:
Dunmail Raise,
Lake District, UK.

Page 94:
Ludlow, UK.

Page 95:
Toll Bar, South
Yorkshire, UK.

Page 95:
Toll Bar, South
Yorkshire, UK.

Page 95:
Tewkesbury, UK.

Page 95:
Toll Bar, South
Yorkshire, UK.

Page 96:
River Derwent,
Workington, UK.

Page 96:
Ambleside, Lake
District, UK.

Page 97:
Keswick, Lake
District, UK.

Page 98:
Cockermouth,
Cumbria, UK.

Page 99:
Ambleside, Lake
District, UK.

Page 99:
Cockermouth,
Cumbria, UK.

Page 100:
Cockermouth,
Cumbria, UK.

Page 100:
Carlisle,
Cumbria, UK.

Page 101:
Pooley Bridge,
Lake District, UK.

Page 101:
Carlisle,
Cumbria, UK.

Page 101:
Carlisle,
Cumbria, UK.

Page 102-103:
Lyth Valley,
Cumbria, UK.

Page 104:
Howtown, Lake
District, UK.

Page 105:
Glenridding, Lake
District, UK.

Page 106:
Appleby,
Cumbria, UK.

Page 106:
A591 at Thirlmere,
Lake District, UK.

Page 107:
St Johns in the Vale,
Lake District, UK.

Page 107:
Shincliffe, near
Durham, UK.

Page 108:
Melbourne,
Australia.

Page 109:
Melbourne,
Australia.

Page 109:
Melbourne,
Australia.

Page 110-111:
Malawi, Africa.

Page 112-113:
Malawi, Africa.

Page 114-115:
Malawi, Africa.

Page 116:
Chikwawa, Malawi.

Page 116:
Between Zomba and
Phalombe, Malawi.

Page 117:
Lower Shire valley,
Malawi.

Page 117:
Bangula, Malawi.

Page 117:
Chikwawa, Malawi.

Page 118:
Bangula, Malawi.

Page 119:
Mulanje, Malawi.

Page 119:
Phalombe, Malawi.

Page 119:
Refugee camp,
Chikwawa, Malawi.

Page 119:
Refugee camp,
Bangula, Malawi.

Page 120:
Phalombe,
Malawi.

Page 121:
Bangula, Malawi.

Page 122:
Bangula, Malawi.

Page 123:
Bangula, Malawi.

Page 123:
Bangula, Malawi.

Page 124:
Chikwawa, Malawi.

Page 125:
Malaria test,
Malawi.

Page 125:
Makhanga, Malawi.

Page 125:
A TV weather
forecast, UK.

Page 125:
Death Valley,
California, USA.

Page 126:
Anti Atlas
Mountains, Morocco.

Page 127:
Anti Atlas
Mountains, Morocco.

Page 128-129:
Tizgui, Anti Atlas
Mountains, Morocco.

Page 130:
Heilongjiang
Province, China.

Page 130:
Shanxi Province,
China.

Page 131:
Shanxi Province,
China.

Page 131:
Dongsheng, Inner
Mongolia, China.

Page 131:
Dongsheng, Inner
Mongolia, China.

Page 132:
Shanxi Province,
China.

Page 132:
Inner Mongolia,
Northern China.

Page 133:
Inner Mongolia,
Northern China.

Page 133:
Shanxi Province,
China.

Page 133:
Near Beijing, China.

Page 134:
Lake Eucumbene
Australia.

Page 135:
Lake Hume,
Australia.

Page 136:
Murray River,
Australia.

Page 136:
Shepperton,
Australia.

Page 137:
Kangaroo skeleton,
Australia.

Page 137:
Snowy Mountains,
Australia.

Page 137:
Shepperton,
Australia.

Page 138-139:
Lake Eildon,
Australia.

Page 235:
Svalbard, Arctic
Ocean.

Page 236:
Gerlache Strait,
Antarctic Peninsular.

Page 237:
Joinville Island,
Antarctic Peninsular.

Page 237:
Curverville Island,
Antarctic Peninsular.

Page 238-239:
Fournier Bay,
Antarctic Peninsular.

Page 242:
Gerlache Strait,
Antarctic Peninsular.

Page 240:
Paradise Bay,
Antarctic Peninsular.

Page 241:
Paradise Bay,
Antarctic Peninsular.

Page 242:
Drygalski Fjord,
Antarctic Peninsular.

Page 243:
Paradise Bay,
Antarctic Peninsular.

Page 244:
Near Anvers Island,
Antarctic Peninsular.

Page 245:
Cairngorm,
Scotland.

Page 245:
Icebergs off the
Greenland Ice Sheet.

Page 246:
Recherchefjorden,
Svalbard.

Page 247:
Fairbanks,
Alaska, USA.

Page 247:
Fairbanks,
Alaska, USA.

Page 248:
Fairbanks,
Alaska, USA.

Page 249:
Fairbanks,
Alaska, USA.

Page 251:
Between Skipsea
and Ulrome, UK.

Page 252:
Island off Funafuti
Atoll, Tuvalu.

Page 252:
Funafuti Atoll,
Tuvalu.

Page 253:
Funafuti Atoll,
Tuvalu.

Page 253:
Funafuti Atoll,
Tuvalu.

Page 254-255:
Tepuka island
off Tuvalu.

Page 256:
Tepuka island
off Tuvalu.

Page 257:
Tepuka island
off Tuvalu.

Page 258:
Funafuti Atoll,
Tuvalu.

Page 258:
Tepukasavilivili,
Tuvalu.

Page 259:
Funafuti Atoll,
Tuvalu.

Page 259:
Tepukasavilivili,
Tuvalu.

Page 260:
Funafuti Atoll,
Tuvalu.

Page 260:
Funafuti Atoll,
Tuvalu.

Page 260:
Funafuti Atoll,
Tuvalu.

Page 261:
Funafuti Atoll,
Tuvalu.

Page 261:
Funafuti Atoll,
Tuvalu.

Page 262:
Coral reef, Funafuti
Atoll, Tuvalu.

Page 263:
Great Barrier Reef,
Australia.

Page 264:
Miami Beach,
Florida.

Page 264:
Miami Beach,
Florida.

Page 265:
Miami Beach,
Florida.

Page 265:
Miami Beach,
Florida.

Page 265:
Dubai, United Arab
Emirates.

Page 266:
Aldbrough,
Yorkshire, UK.

Page 267:
Aldbrough,
Yorkshire, UK.

Page 268:
Cley next the Sea,
Norfolk, UK.

Page 269:
Happisburgh,
Norfolk, UK.

Page 269:
Happisburgh,
Norfolk, UK.

Page 270:
Humber
Estuary, UK.

Page 271:
Humber
Estuary, UK.

Page 272:
Storth, Kent Estuary,
Cumbria, UK.

Page 273:
Storth, Kent Estuary,
Cumbria, UK.

Page 274-275:
Ganges Delta, India.

Page 276:
Amsterdam,
Netherlands.

Page 276:
Amsterdam,
Netherlands.

Page 276:
Amsterdam,
Netherlands.

Page 277:
Amsterdam,
Netherlands.

Page 322:
Boudanath Stupa,
Kathmandu, Nepal.

Page 323:
The Sunderbans,
Ganges Delta, India.

Page 323:
Funafuti Atoll
Tuvalu.

Page 323:
Funafuti Atoll
Tuvalu.

Page 323:
Shishmaref, Alaska.

Page 324:
Aboriginal woman,
Nr Cairns, Australia.

Page 324:
Fort Chipewyan,
Canada.

Page 324:
Anti Atlas
Mountains, Morocco.

Page 324:
Anti Atlas
Mountains, Morocco.

Page 325:
Sinai Desert near
Dahab, Egypt.

Page 326:
Efthalou, Lesvos,
Greece.

Page 326:
Mytilini, Lesvos,
Greece.

Page 326:
Mytilini, Lesvos,
Greece.

Page 327:
Efthalou, Lesvos,
Greece.

Page 327:
Efthalou, Lesvos,
Greece.

Page 328-329
Efthalou, Lesvos,
Greece.

Page 331:
The Wave Protest,
London, UK.

Page 332:
Fort McMurray,
Alberta, Canada.

Page 332:
Fort McMurray,
Alberta, Canada.

Page 333:
Little Plumpton,
near Blackpool, UK.

Page 333:
Heathrow Airport,
London, UK.

Page 333:
Demonstration,
Lancashire, UK.

Page 334:
Protestors,
London, UK.

Page 334:
Parliament Square,
London, UK.

Page 334:
Climate Change
Protest, London, UK.

Page 335:
The Wave Protest,
London, UK.

Page 336-337:
Near Parliament,
London, UK.

Page 338:
American Embassy,
London, UK.

Page 339:
Fracking Protestors,
Blackpool, UK.

Page 339:
Barrow in Furness
Cumbria, UK.

Page 341:
Mojave Desert,
California, USA.

Page 342:
Dryholme Farm,
Silloth, Cumbria, UK.

Page 342:
An Algae Link
System.

Page 342:
Dryholme Farm,
Silloth, Cumbria, UK.

Page 343:
Lockerbie, Scotland,
UK.

Page 343:
The Sunderbans,
Ganges Delta, India.

Page 344:
Cley next the Sea,
North Norfolk, UK.

Page 344:
Almere, Flevoland,
Netherlands.

Page 345:
Almere, Flevoland,
Netherlands.

Page 345:
Kirkstone Pass, Lake
District, UK.

Page 345:
Tehachapi Pass,
California, USA.

Page 346-347:
Tehachapi Pass,
California, USA.

Page 348:
Isle of Eigg,
Scotland.

Page 349:
Isle of Eigg,
Scotland.

Page 350:
Eaglesham Moor,
Glasgow, Scotland.

Page 350:
Barrow-in-Furness,
Cumbria, UK.

Page 350:
Barrow-in-Furness,
Cumbria, UK.

Page 351:
Barrow-in-Furness,
Cumbria, UK.

Page 351:
Barrow-in-Furness,
Cumbria, UK.

Page 352-353:
Offshore, Barrow-
in-Furness, UK.

Page 354-355:
Barrow-in-Furness,
Cumbria, UK.

Page 356:
Offshore, Barrow-
in-Furness, UK.

Page 357:
Offshore, Barrow-
in-Furness, UK.

Page 357:
Offshore, Barrow-
in-Furness, UK.

Page 358:
Offshore, Barrow-
in-Furness, UK.

Page 358:
Gunfleet Sands,
Essex, UK.

Page 359:
Seaton, Workington,
Cumbria, UK.

Page 359:
Antequera,
Andalucia, Spain.

Page 359:
Workington,
Cumbria, UK.

Page 359:
Rydal, Lake District,
UK.

Page 360:
Rydal, Lake District,
UK.

Page 361:
Snowy Mountains,
Australia.

Page 362:
Vatnajokull, Iceland.

Page 363:
Vatnajokull, Iceland.

Page 364:
Blue Lagoon,
Keflavik, Iceland.

Page 364:
Geyser, Iceland

Page 364:
Hengill, Iceland.

Page 365:
Hveragerdi, Iceland.

Page 365:
Northern Lights,
Iceland.

Page 366:
Kirkwall, Orkney,
UK.

Page 366:
Reykavik, Iceland.

Page 366:
Lyness on Hoy,
Orkney, UK.

Page 367:
Newcastle, UK.

Page 368:
Cabanne d'Orny,
Switzerland.

Page 368:
Almere,
Netherlands.

Page 369:
Ambleside, Lake
District, UK.

Page 370:
Sanlucar La Mayor,
Andalucia, Spain.

Page 370:
Guadix, Andalucia,
Spain.

Page 370:
Sanlucar La Mayor,
Andalucia, Spain.

Page 371:
Sanlucar La Mayor,
Andalucia, Spain.

Page 371:
Sanlucar La Mayor,
Andalucia, Spain.

Page 372:
Caravaca, Andalucia,
Spain.

Page 373:
Sanlucar La Mayor,
Andalucia, Spain.

Page 374:
Mojave Desert,
California, USA.

Page 375:
Mojave Desert,
California, USA.

Page 376:
Godley Reservoir,
Manchester, UK.

Page 377:
Near Suihua City,
China.

Page 378:
The Sundarbans,
Ganges Delta, India.

Page 378:
The Sundarbans,
Ganges Delta, India.

Page 378:
The Sundarbans,
Ganges Delta, India.

Page 379:
The Sundarbans,
Ganges Delta, India.

Page 380:
The Sundarbans,
Ganges Delta, India.

Page 380:
Bangalore,
Karnataka, India.

Page 380-381:
Goraj, near
Vadodara, India.

Page 382:
Muni Seva Ashram,
Goraj, India.

Page 383:
Muni Seva Ashram,
Goraj, India.

Page 383:
Muni Seva Ashram,
Goraj, India.

Page 384:
Tilonia, Rajasthan,
India.

Page 384:
Tilonia, Rajasthan,
India.

Page 385:
Tilonia, Rajasthan,
India.

Page 386:
Tilonia, Rajasthan,
India.

Page 387:
Annapurna Base
Camp, Nepal.

Page 389:
Heathrow Airport,
London, UK.

Page 391:
Climate Change
Rally, London, UK.

Page 392-393:
Amsterdam,
Netherlands.

Page 394:
Yosemite Nat Park,
California, USA.

Page 395:
Climate Change
Rally, London, UK.

Page 396:
A message to
the earth.

Page 397:
Near Parliament,
London, UK.

Page 412-413:
World map showing
project destinations.

Back endpapers:
Oil on water, on a
tarmac road.

Key to world map

1	Shishmaref, Alaska, USA.	37	Scrabster, Scotland, UK.	74	Harbin, Heilongjiang, China.
2	Nome, Alaska, USA.	38	Isle of Eigg, Scotland, UK.	75	Inner Mongolia, China.
3	Seward, Alaska, USA.	39	Glasgow, UK.	76	Beijing, China.
4	Fairbanks, Alaska, USA.	40	Newcastle upon Tyne, UK.	77	Seoul, South Korea.
5	Jasper, Alberta, Canada.	41	Snowdonia, UK.	78	Cairns, Australia.
6	Fort McMurray, Alberta, Canada.	42	Happisburgh, UK.	79	Great Barrier Reef, Australia.
7	Fort Chipewyan, Alberta, Canada.	43	Wadebridge, UK.	80	Tuvalu.
8	Camp Victor, Greenland.	44	London, UK.	81	Fiji.
9	Ilulissat, Greenland.	45	Amsterdam, Netherlands.	82	Sydney, Australia.
10	El Dorado Forest California, USA.	46	Copenhagen, Denmark.	83	Melbourne, Australia.
11	Las Vagas, Nevada, USA.	47	Cabanne d'Orny, Switzerland.	84	Lake Eildon, Australia.
12	Bakersfield, California, USA.	48	Chamonix, France.	85	Lebourne, Australia
13	New York, USA.	49	The Dolomites, Italy.		
14	Miami, Florida, USA.,	50	Venice.		
15	Chacaltaya, Bolivia.	51	Slovenia.		
16	La Paz, Bolivia.	52	Andorra.		
17	Buenos Aires, Argentina.	53	Barcelona, Spain.		
18	Falkland Islands.	54	Sanlucar La Mayor, Andalucia, Spain.		
19	Ushuaia, Argentina	55	Guadix, Andalucia, Spain.		
20	South Georgia.	56	Sivota, Greece.		
21	Antarctic Peninsular.	57	Lesbos, Greece		
22	Antarctic Peninsular.	58	Teos, Turkey.		
23	Arctic Ocean (500 miles from the North Pole)	59	Crete.		
24	Sorgfjorden, Svalbard.	60	Anti Atlas Mountains, Morocco.		
25	Julibukta, Svalbard.	61	Anti Atlas Mountains, Morocco.		
26	Vibebukta, Svalbard.	62	Dahab, Egypt.		
27	Rechercheffjorden, Svalbard.	63	Zomba, Malawi.		
28	Tromoso, Norway.	64	Blantyre, Malawi.		
29	Saariselka, Finland.	65	Makhanga, Malawi.		
30	Husavik, Iceland.	66	Dubai, United Arab Emirates.		
31	Saudarkrokur, Iceland.	67	Rajasthan, India.		
32	Reykjavik, Iceland.	68	New Delhi, India.		
33	Vik, Iceland.	69	Annapurna, Nepal.		
34	Hofn, Iceland.	70	Kathmandu, Nepal.		
35	The Orkney Islands, UK.	71	The Sunderbans, India.		
36	Lewis, Outer Hebrides, UK.	72	Bangalore, India.		
		73	Chinese/Russian Border.		

Following pages:

Map of the world showing destinations.

Oil on water, on a tarmac road.